go further with

INVESTIGATIONS

For National Curriculum levels 3-6

SPECTRUM MATHS

Dave Kirkby

CollinsEducational
An imprint of HarperCollinsPublishers

Acknowledgements

The author and publisher would like to thank
Ann Nimmo, John Walker and Anne Woodman
for their helpful comments on the Spectrum
Maths material.

This Edition 1992 by
CollinsEducational
77–85 Fulham Palace Road
Hammersmith London W6 8JB
First published 1989 by Unwin Hyman Ltd, London
Reprinted 1993

British Library Cataloguing in Publication Data
Kirkby, Dave
    Spectrum mathematics.
    : Go further with investigations.
    1. Mathematics, for schools.
    I. Title
    510

ISBN 0 00 312542 4

Designed and illustrated by AMR, Basingstoke
Typeset by Microset Graphics Ltd, Basingstoke
Printed in Great Britain at The Alden Press, Oxford
Bound by Hunter & Foulis Ltd, Edinburgh

Contents

Content Focus

Topic	Starting Investigations	More Investigations	Go Further With Investigations
Addition	2, 3, 7, 9, 10, 12, 15, 17, 19, 24, 25, 29, 30, 31, 33, 35, 38	2, 11, 21, 25, 32, 36, 37	1, 17, 19, 28, 32
Subtraction	14, 39	17	5, 7
Multiplication		6, 7, 8, 12, 33	4, 12, 13, 24, 29, 36, 37
Division			9, 25, 40
Mixed number operations		29	16, 21, 33
Place value	40	1, 13, 16, 28	
Odds and evens	1, 23		
Decimals			20
Number patterns	8, 13, 28, 36	8, 19, 21, 32, 36, 37	3, 8, 13, 17, 24, 29, 31, 38, 40
Money	7, 15, 19, 38		
Colour patterns	4, 22, 26, 27, 34		
Shape patterns	4, 8, 11, 20, 32, 37	5, 9, 18, 20, 22, 23, 24, 26, 27, 39, 40	2, 10, 15, 26, 34, 39
Shape	5	15	
Triangles			11, 14, 35
Squares		4	31
Rectangles	21	30	
Polygons		3, 14, 35	6, 23, 30
Cubes			18
Symmetry		10	
Area	6, 16, 18	12, 31, 27	22, 27
Perimeter		12, 38	22.

Apparatus Focus

Apparatus	Starting Investigations	More Investigations	Go Further With Investigations
Calculators			4, 29, 33, 36
Calendars		37	17
Card			18
Circles			34
Coins	7, 15, 19, 38		
Counters	27, 28	24	
Cubes	8, 13, 20, 34	34	38
Dice	23, 25, 39	2, 33	
Dominoes	1, 3, 30		
Geobards		4, 31	6, 11, 23, 27
Hexagons	32		
Mirrors		10	
Number balance	12		
Number cards	2, 10, 14, 17, 29, 40	1, 7, 11, 13, 16, 17, 25, 28	1, 5, 12, 16, 20, 21, 25, 32, 36, 37
Number rods	21, 24, 31, 33, 36, 37	21	
Operation cards			16, 21, 25
Polygons			8
Rectangles	4, 9, 11	14	
Scissors	5		
Scrap paper	5		
Squares	22	3, 9. 26, 38, 40	3, 10, 22, 26, 30
Triangles		22	

Using the Teacher's Notes

CONTENT

This heading states the focus of the investigation in terms of a particular mathematical topic, e.g. Triangles, Addition, Number patterns.
A more detailed description of the potential content is outlined here on each of the teacher's pages.

Apparatus

This section indicates to the teacher what apparatus is likely to be required for the investigation, e.g. Cubes or Number cards. Where appropriate, the teacher is alerted to the availability, at the back of the book, of a 'special paper' which the pupils can use to record their work.

LEVEL	Profile Component 1				Profile Component 2		
	UA	N	A	M	UA	S	D
1							
2							
3							
4							
5							
6							
7							
8							
9							
10							

Key: UA – Using and Applying Mathematics.
N – Number.
A – Algebra.
M – Measures.
S – Shape and Space.
D – Handling Data.

The teacher's notes for each investigation contain the above table. This table refers to the attainment targets and levels of the National Curriculum. An attempt has been made to locate, by means of dots in the table, the approximate content level for each investigation, but it must be appreciated that many activities can be performed at a variety of different levels.

This section contains the teaching notes but not necessarily the answers. The notes are intended as a guide to the possible directions the investigation may take. They contain background mathematics for the teacher, but should not be seen as an indication of what can be expected from all pupils. The pupils should feel free to follow their own lines of enquiry, which may very well not coincide with these notes.

This section may also include suggestions about recording, points for discussion, warnings, etcetera

QUESTIONS

These suggested follow-up questions may lead to further investigations. They may also provide teachers with some ideas for potential areas for development. Many of the investigations are rich in opportunities for introducing a variety of mathematical ideas. Questions can help to link different ideas and concepts. Although the questions are written simply, teachers may need to adapt the phrasing and language to suit their pupils.

EXTENSIONS

→ It is hoped that pupils will develop sufficient interest and confidence to extend their work in their own way.

→ This section contains suggestions that teachers may wish to use with particular pupils, whilst encouraging them to develop their own ideas.

Using the Pupils' Sheets

You will need

The basic information about apparatus also appears on the pupils' sheets, so that the children have some idea of what materials they need.

The pupils' sheets are written using as few words as possible. However, pupils may still need some help in getting started.

Find or **Investigate** precedes an indication of where to start. Sometimes the indication is deliberately vague.

Encourage the pupils to become responsible for their own lines of enquiry, and to extend them in some way.

INTRODUCTION

Most schools use a mathematics scheme. Teachers using these require a range of support material to supplement the scheme. Such material is provided by **Spectrum Maths.**

```
INVESTIGATIONS
SPECTRUM
MATHS
```

This is a series of three books of investigations primarily for the primary years, although secondary school teachers with low attaining pupils will also find these books useful.

They are defined in terms of three ability levels. Broadly defined, these levels are:

Starting Investigations (Infants)
More Investigations (Lower Juniors)
Go Further With Investigations (Upper Juniors)

Each book contains:

40 pupil investigations in the form of photocopymasters.
Detailed teacher notes accompanying each investigation.
Special papers in the form of photocopymasters to aid pupils to record their work.

HOW CAN IT BE USED?

Spectrum Maths investigations can be used in a variety of ways:

(a) to consolidate other work in the school mathematics scheme
(b) as a completely separate supplement to the scheme
(c) as a means of introducing a new topic within the scheme
(d) to provide enrichment material at appropriate times.

The 40 pupil investigations in each book are non-sequential.
Investigations can be selected by the teacher to suit individual needs.
The teacher's notes contain clear indications of both the **content** area and the required **apparatus** for each investigation. This will aid the teacher who wishes to be selective. Some teachers may wish to select a group of investigations based on a particular mathematical theme e.g. **multiplication**. Others may choose investigations requiring the use of a particular piece of apparatus e.g. **cubes**.

The material is flexible in terms of organisation.
Some examples include:

Individual investigations: pupils working individually on their own particular investigation.

Small group investigations: the class divided into groups, each group working on a different investigation.

Class investigation: the whole class working on the same investigation. This may be the easiest form of organisation for teachers who are starting on this type of work.

School investigation: several classes working on the same investigation. This enables teachers to discuss and compare experiences amongst each other. It can also lead to combined work displays.

WHAT IS AN INVESTIGATION?

An **investigation** presents pupils with an open mathematical situation and invites them to explore it.

In most mathematical activities, a goal is specified and an answer is sought. There is no 'answer' to an investigation. It is the 'journey', not the 'destination' which is the goal.

The **Spectrum investigations** pupil material provides guidelines and suggestions of ways in which the pupil explorations may lead, and ideas for helping pupils continue their 'journey'.

As pupils become practised in making 'journeys' they will need to experience some of the following:

> understanding the starting point
> trying some examples
> recording results (diagrams, tables, drawings, lists etc.)
> devising methods of recording
> spotting patterns
> describing patterns
> checking results
> generalising results
> systematically organising the 'journey'
> devising strategies
> writing an account of the 'journey'
> extending the 'journey'

The 'journey' is often referred to as 'mathematical process' and lists like those above as 'process objectives'.

CALCULATORS

Spectrum Mathematics: Investigations does not contain many activities which focus on the use of a calculator. Nevertheless, pupils will often find a calculator a valuable aid, particularly when extending an investigation. The provision of calculators is left to the discretion of the teacher.

The activities which a calculator may be required are:

Starting Investigations 2, 7, 8, 10, 15, 17, 19, 25, 33, 35, 38.

More Investigations 2, 7, 11, 12, 17, 21, 25, 29, 32, 33, 37.

Go Further With Investigations 1, 4, 5, 7, 9, 12, 13, 16, 17, 19, 21, 25, 29, 33, 36, 40.

1 Sum hope

ADDITION

Addition of three two-digit numbers.
Finding the different totals possible using six given digits.

Apparatus

Use cards numbered 1 to 9.

LEVEL	Profile Component 1				Profile Component 2		
	UA	N	A	M	UA	S	D
1							
2							●
3	●		●				
4	●	●	●				
5	●						
6	●						
7							
8							
9							
10							

N4: Addition of two-digit numbers.
A3: Number patterns.
A4: Generalise patterns in words.
D2: Recording results.

There are twelve different possible totals:

16	14	14	13	14	13
37	37	36	46	36	46
+ 49	+ 69	+ 79	+ 79	+ 97	+ 97
102	120	129	138	147	156

13	13	31	31	41	61
64	74	64	74	73	73
+ 97	+ 96	+ 97	+ 96	+ 96	+ 94
174	183	192	201	210	228

In each case, various different arrangements of the digits will produce the same total.

QUESTIONS

(?) What is the smallest/greatest possible total?

(?) How many different totals are there altogether?

(?) Can you find an arrangement to total 120?

(?) What is the digital sum of each total?

EXTENSIONS

(→) Try with a different set of cards.

(→) Try exploring different arrangements of the digits which give a total of 102.

(→) Try with a different arrangement, e.g.

Sum hope

You will need these cards

| 1 | 3 | 4 | 6 | 7 | 9 |

Place them in this **addition sum** and find the **total**.

Examples

```
  1 4        4 1
  3 6        7 3
+ 7 9      + 9 6
-----      -----
  129        210
```

How many different **totals** can you find?

SHAPE PATTERNS

Different ways of dividing a 4 x 4 square grid in half. Area. Symmetry.

Apparatus

Use squared paper for drawing the grids and illustrating the cuts.

LEVEL	Profile Component 1				Profile Component 2		
	UA	N	A	M	UA	S	D
1							
2						●	●
3						●	●
4				●		●	●
5						●	
6						●	
7							
8							
9							
10							

M4: Area.
S2: Recognise rotations.
S3: Sorting shapes in different ways.
S4: Constructing shapes.
D2: Recording and classifying results.

The different cuts can be separated into types:

Horizontal and vertical lines only

Sloping lines only

Combinations of horizontal, vertical and sloping lines

QUESTIONS

(?) What is the area of the starting grid?

(?) What is the area of each half?

(?) Which cuts look the same upside down?

EXTENSIONS

(→) Try different sized starting grids.

(→) Try cutting grids into four.

Half-cut

You will need

squared paper

Start with a 4 x 4 **square**.

Find ways of cutting it in **half**.

Here are three ways:

Find other ways of cutting the square in **half**.

go further with
INVESTIGATIONS
SPECTRUM MATHS

3 Folding square

NUMBER PATTERNS

Folding a 3 x 3 square arrangement of digits to produce
two-digit numbers. Finding all possible positions for the folds.

Apparatus

Square pieces of paper (approximately 15 cm x 15 cm) are
required.

LEVEL	Profile Component 1				Profile Component 2		
	UA	N	A	M	UA	S	D
1							
2						●	●
3	●		●		●		
4	●				●		
5	●		●		●		
6	●				●		
7							
8							
9							
10							

A3: Number patterns.
A5: Primes, multiples.
S2: Creating patterns through folding a square.
D2: Recording observations.

There are 32 possible two-digit arrangements.
These 24 are relatively easy to find:

8 3	3 6	9 2	2 5	8 9	5 6	6 5	9 8
5 4	4 9	4 6	6 8	5 4	8 9	9 8	4 5
2 7	7 1	1 7	7 3	2 1	3 1	1 3	1 2

These 8 are more difficult:

9 2	2 9	5 1	1 5	3 6	6 3	1 8	8 1

The two-digit numbers can then be tabulated according to first digits:

1	2	3	4	5	6	7	8	9
12	21	31	45	51	63	71	81	92
13	25	36	46	54	65	73	83	(92)
15	27	(36)	49	(54)	68		89	98
17	29			56			(89)	(98)
18								

The ringed numbers are repeats. So there are 27 different two-digit numbers.

QUESTIONS

(?) What is the smallest/greatest two-digit
number?

(?) How many numbers between 60 and 70 can be
found?

(?) Which numbers can be found in different
ways?

(?) How many numbers with a units digit of 1 can
be found?

EXTENSIONS

(→) Try with a different arrangement of
digits.

(→) Try with a 4 x 4 square.

(→) Try exploring the sum of the two
digits.

Folding square

You will need

a large piece of paper (about 15 cm x 15 cm).

Draw a 3 x 3 grid.
Crease along the lines.

Write these numbers in the squares.

9	**2**	**5**
4	**6**	**8**
1	**7**	**3**

Front

8	3	6
5	4	9
2	7	1

Back

Fold the paper to show two **horizontal digits.**

6	8

— the number 68

4	5

— the number 45

How many other **two-digit numbers** can you find?

4   Top brick

MULTIPLICATION

Multiplication facts.

Apparatus

Calculators may be necessary for some of the harder multiplications, especially when larger numbers are written on all the starting bricks.

LEVEL	Profile Component 1				Profile Component 2		
	UA	N	A	M	UA	S	D
1							
2							●
3	●		●				
4	●	●					
5	●						
6	●						
7							
8							
9							
10							

N4: Multiplication facts up to 10 x 10.
A3: Number patterns.
D2: Recording outcomes.

One strategy is to consider different centre numbers in the first layer, and then the different possible combinations for the other two numbers:

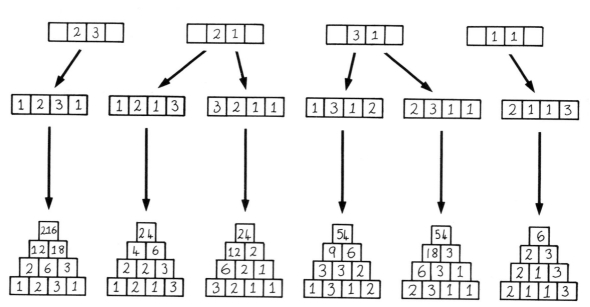

So, there are only four different top bricks: 6, 24, 54, 216.

QUESTIONS

(?)   Which bottom row gives the smallest/greatest number on the top brick?

(?)   Which bottom rows give the same number on the top brick?

EXTENSIONS

(→)   Try with different numbers on the starting bricks.

(→)   Try with pyramids of different sizes, e.g.

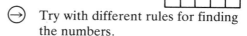

(→)   Try with different rules for finding the numbers.

Top brick

You will need

a calculator

Start with a line of four bricks numbered 1, 1, 2, 3.

2	1	3	1

To find the numbers on the next row of bricks, multiply like this. ➞

2	**3**	**3**
2	1	3	1

2x1=**2**   1x3=**3**   3x1=**3**

Build a **pyramid**.

54

6	9

2	3	3

2	1	3	1

The **top brick** is 54 .

Now put the bottom bricks in different places and build other pyramids.

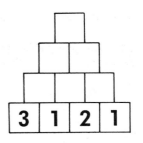

3	**1**	**2**	**1**

Try with **different** numbers in the **bottom** row.

go further with
INVESTIGATIONS
SPECTRUM MATHS

5 Take-away time

SUBTRACTION

Subtraction of a two-digit number from another two-digit number. Searching for all the possible answers, using four given digits.

Apparatus

Use cards numbered 1 to 9.

LEVEL	Profile Component 1				Profile Component 2		
	UA	N	A	M	UA	S	D
1							
2							●
3	●		●				
4	●	●					
5	●						
6	●						
7							
8							
9							
10							

N4: Subtracting two two-digit numbers.
A3: Number patterns in subtraction.
D2: Recording results.

The possible arrangements are:

$$
\begin{array}{cccccc}
54 & 53 & 57 & 57 & 45 & 47 \\
-\,37 & -\,47 & -\,34 & -\,43 & -\,37 & -\,35 \\
\hline
17 & 6 & 23 & 14 & 8 & 12
\end{array}
$$

$$
\begin{array}{cccccc}
73 & 73 & 74 & 74 & 75 & 75 \\
-\,45 & -\,54 & -\,53 & -\,35 & -\,34 & -\,43 \\
\hline
28 & 19 & 21 & 39 & 41 & 32
\end{array}
$$

Some discussion is necessary to eliminate arrangements such as
$$
\begin{array}{c}
37 \\
-\,45 \\
\hline
\end{array}
$$

Alternatively, some pupils may wish to investigate negative answers.

So, there are 12 different answers:

6, 8, 12, 14, 17, 19, 21, 23, 28, 32, 39 and 41.

QUESTIONS

(?) How many different answers can be found?

(?) Which is the smallest/greatest possible answer?

(?) Can you find an arrangement with the answer 12?

EXTENSIONS

(→) Try with a different set of digits.

(→) Try with two digits the same, e.g. 3, 4, 4, 7.

(→) Try with three-digit numbers.

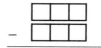

Take-away time

You will need these cards

| 3 | 4 | 5 | 7 |

Place them here.

Subtract to find the **answer**.

Examples

$$\begin{array}{cc} \boxed{5} & \boxed{7} \\ - \boxed{3} & \boxed{4} \\ \hline 2 & 3 \end{array} \qquad \begin{array}{cc} \boxed{7} & \boxed{5} \\ - \boxed{3} & \boxed{4} \\ \hline 4 & 1 \end{array}$$

How many different **answers** can you find?

go further with
INVESTIGATIONS
SPECTRUM MATHS

6 **Parallels**

Drawing polygons with parallel sides on a 3 x 3 square dotty grid. Naming polygons: square, rectangle, parallelogram, trapezium, pentagon, hexagon.

Apparatus

Use a geoboard for making the different shapes, which can then be recorded on special paper 4.

LEVEL	Profile Component 1				Profile Component 2		
	UA	N	A	M	UA	S	D
1							
2							
3						●	●
4				●		●	●
5						●	●
6						●	●
7							
8							
9							
10							

M4: Area.
S3: Sorting 2D shapes in different ways. Symmetry.
S4: Constructing different shapes. Parallels.
S5: Congruence of simple shapes.
S6: Classifying types of quadrilaterals.

One approach is to consider shapes with one pair of parallel sides, then two pairs, and so on.

Some possibilities include:

1 pair

2 pairs

3 pairs

(?) What is the name of each shape? (Square, parallelogram, etc.)

(?) Which shapes are symmetrical?

(?) What is the area of each shape?

(→) Try making shapes on a 3 x 4 grid.

(→) Try making shapes with no parallel sides.

Parallels

You will need

**square dotty paper
a 3 x 3 geoboard**

This shape has **one pair
of parallel sides.**

This shape has **two pairs
of parallel sides.**

Find some more shapes with **parallel sides.**

go *further with*
INVESTIGATIONS
**SPECTRUM
MATHS**

Up the wall

SUBTRACTION

Differences between two single-digit numbers, extending possibly to differences between two two-digit numbers.

Apparatus

Use special paper 2 for the walls.

LEVEL	Profile Component 1				Profile Component 2		
	UA	N	A	M	UA	S	D
1							
2							●
3	●	●					
4	●	●					
5	●						
6	●						
7							
8							
9							
10							

N3: Subtraction facts up to 20.
N4: Subtraction of two two-digit numbers.
D2: Recording results.

The wall ends with ☐ 0 ☐ 0 ☐ 0 ☐ 0 ☐.

```
        0 0 0 0
       1 1 1 1
      2 1 2 1
     2 4 5 3
    5 3 7 2
```

Here are some other examples:

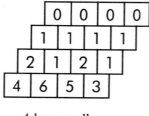

4-layer wall

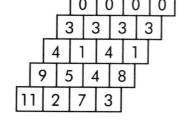

5-layer wall

Pupils can try to find walls of different heights.

QUESTIONS

(?) Do all walls end in ☐ 0 ☐ 0 ☐ 0 ☐ 0 ☐ ?

(?) Does the starting arrangement make any difference?

(?) Is it possible to make a wall with more than 6 layers?

EXTENSIONS

(→) Try with larger numbers, e.g. 32, 48, 61, 75.

(→) Try with 3 starting numbers, then 5 starting numbers.

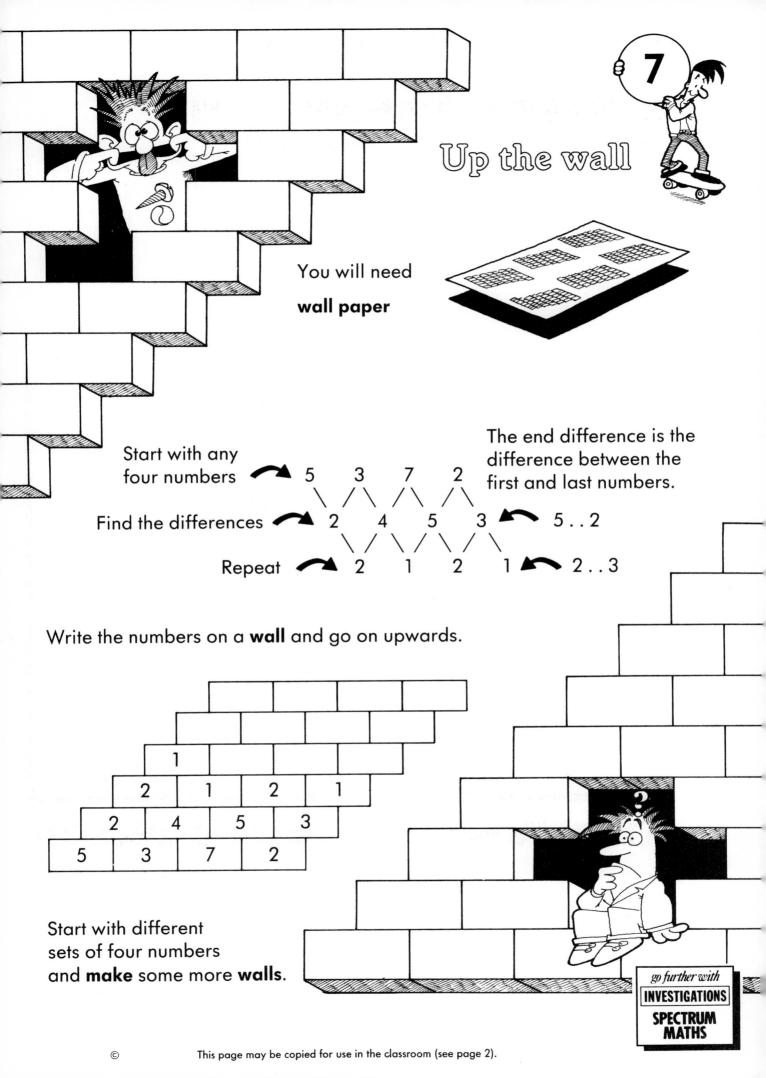

Up the wall

You will need

wall paper

Start with any
four numbers → 5   3   7   2

The end difference is the difference between the first and last numbers.

Find the differences → 2   4   5   3 ← 5 . . 2

Repeat → 2   1   2   1 ← 2 . . 3

Write the numbers on a **wall** and go on upwards.

		1		
	2	1	2	1
2	4	5	3	
5	3	7	2	

Start with different
sets of four numbers
and **make** some more **walls**.

Hexagon cut

NUMBER PATTERNS

Patterns in the numbers of diagonals in polygons with varying numbers of sides.

Apparatus

Use templates of regular hexagons for drawing the outlines. Regular pentagons and octagons will also be useful.

LEVEL	Profile Component 1				Profile Component 2		
	UA	N	A	M	UA	S	D
1							
2							●
3	●		●				
4	●		●			●	
5	●						
6	●						
7							
8							
9							
10							

A3: Explaining and predicting number patterns.
A4: Generalise patterns in words.
S4: Constructing shapes.
D2: Recording data.

The diagonals look like this.

There are 6 vertices, and 3 lines drawn from each.
6 x 3 = 18 lines

Each line has been counted twice (both ends). So the total number of diagonals is 9.

For   a 5-sided polygon, the number of diagonals is   5.
For   a 6-sided polygon, the number of diagonals is   9.
For   a 7-sided polygon, the number of diagonals is 14.
For an 8-sided polygon, the number of diagonals is 20.

Generally, for an n-sided polygon there are $\dfrac{n(n-3)}{2}$ diagonals.

2

QUESTIONS

(?)   Are all the diagonals the same length?

(?)   What do you notice if you rotate the drawing?

(?)   Where do lots of diagonals meet?

EXTENSIONS

(→)   Try colouring a pattern in the completed drawing.

(→)   Try a non-regular hexagon.

(→)   Try polygons with different numbers of sides.

(→)   Try investigating the number of intersections of the diagonals.

(→)   Try investigating the number of regions produced.

Hexagon cut

You will need

polygon templates

Draw a regular **hexagon**.

Now start to draw some **diagonals**.

Draw all the diagonals you can.
Find the total number of **diagonals**.

Repeat with some other **polygons**.

go further with
INVESTIGATIONS
SPECTRUM MATHS

9 Factors

DIVISION

Divisors or factors of different numbers.
Prime numbers. Square numbers.

LEVEL	Profile Component 1				Profile Component 2		
	UA	N	A	M	UA	S	D
1							
2							●
3	●						●
4	●	●					●
5	●		●				
6	●						
7							
8							
9							
10							

N4: Division.
A5: Multiples. Factors. Prime numbers.
   Square numbers.
D2: Recording data in a table.
D3: Extracting information from a table.
D4: Grouping and ordering data.

Pupils could start by making a list.

Number	Factors	Total
1	1	1
2	1, 2	2
3	1, 3	2
4	1, 2, 4	3
5	1, 5	2
6	1, 2, 3, 6	4
7	1, 7	2
8	1, 2, 4, 8	4
9	1, 3, 9	3
10	1, 2, 5, 10	4

Number	Factors	Total
11	1, 11	2
12	1, 2, 3, 4, 6, 12	6
13	1, 13	2
14	1, 2, 7, 14	4
15	1, 3, 5, 15	4
16	1, 2, 4, 8, 16	5
17	1, 17	2
18	1, 2, 3, 6, 9, 18	6
19	1, 19	2
20	1, 2, 4, 5, 10, 20	6

Numbers with:
2 factors — 2, 3, 5, 7, 11, 13, 17, 19 — Prime numbers
3 factors — 4, 9, 25, 49   — Square numbers
4 factors — 6, 8, 10, 14, 15
5 factors — 16, 81   — Square numbers
6 factors — 12, 18, 20, 28, 32

Numbers with 3 factors are the squares of prime numbers.

QUESTIONS

(?) Which numbers have 2 factors?

(?) Which number has the most factors?

(?) Can you find a number with 8 factors; 10 factors; . . .?

(?) What numbers have an odd number of factors?

EXTENSIONS

(→) Try extending the lists of numbers.

(→) Try summing the factors of a number.

Factors

8 has 4 **factors.** **1, 2, 4, 8**

13 has 2 **factors.** **1, 13**

9 has 3 **factors.** **1, 3, 9**

Find the **factors** of other numbers.

go further with
INVESTIGATIONS
SPECTRUM MATHS

Big square

SHAPE PATTERNS

Making different patterns based on 4 half-coloured squares.
Symmetry. Conservation of area.

Apparatus

Colour half of each of four card squares for use in making the
different patterns.
Use special paper 1 for recording.

LEVEL	Profile Component 1				Profile Component 2		
	UA	N	A	M	UA	S	D
1							
2						●	●
3					●	●	
4					●		
5					●		
6					●		
7							
8							
9							
10							

S2: Creating patterns.
S3: Sorting patterns in different ways.
Symmetry.
D2: Recording patterns. Choosing
classification criteria.

The patterns can be divided into types:

Square patterns

Cross patterns

Diagonal patterns

QUESTIONS

(?) What is the area of the coloured part of each
pattern?

(?) Which patterns are symmetrical?

(?) How many lines of symmetry does each
pattern have?

EXTENSIONS

(→) Try exploring patterns in a 4 x 1
rectangle.

(→) Try with squares which are
three-quarters coloured.

(→) Try with   to make circular
patterns.

Big square

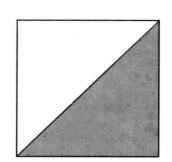

You will need

squares
big squares paper

Make 4 **squares** like this.

Place them in this **big square** to make **patterns**.

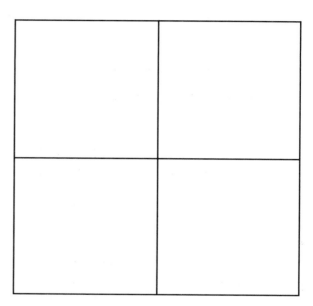

Here are two:

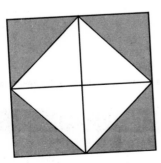 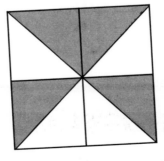

Make some other **patterns.**

go further with
INVESTIGATIONS
SPECTRUM MATHS

Triangles

TRIANGLES

Making different triangles on a 3 x 3 geoboard. Types of triangle: right-angled, isosceles, acute-angled, obtuse-angled. Rotations and reflections.

Apparatus

Use a geoboard for making the different shapes, which can then be recorded on special paper 4.

LEVEL	Profile Component 1				Profile Component 2		
	UA	N	A	M	UA	S	D
1							
2						●	●
3					●	●	
4					●	●	
5					●	●	
6					●		
7							
8							
9							
10							

S2: Recognition of rotations and reflections.
S3: Sorting shapes.
S4: Constructing different shapes.
S5: Congruence of simple shapes.
     Angle properties of triangles.
D2: Recording results.

It is probably easier to assume that reflections and rotations of a shape are identical to the original shape.

e.g.
 and identical to

Then there are 8 different triangles:

The triangles could be labelled; right-angled, isosceles, etc.

QUESTIONS

(?) Which triangles are right-angled?

(?) Which triangles are isosceles?

(?) Which triangles are symmetrical?

(?) Which triangle has the smallest/largest area?

EXTENSIONS

(→) Try exploring different positions of the same triangle.

(→) Try making quadrilaterals on a 3 x 3 board.

(→) Try making triangles on other boards, e.g. 3 x 4, 4 x 4.

Triangles

You will need

**square dotty paper
a 3 x 3 geoboard**

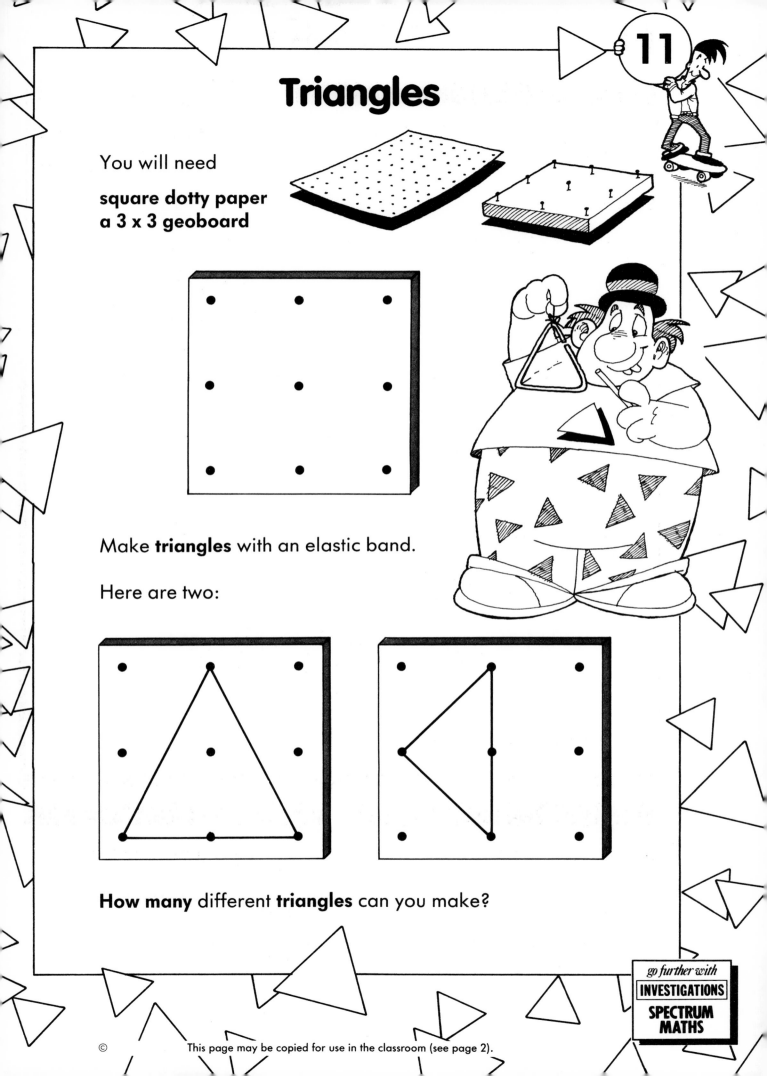

Make **triangles** with an elastic band.

Here are two:

How many different **triangles** can you make?

go further with
INVESTIGATIONS

**SPECTRUM
MATHS**

12 Times square

MULTIPLICATION

Multiplication facts up to 10 x 10.
Arrangements of four different cards in a 2 x 2 square.

Apparatus

Use cards numbered 1 to 10.

LEVEL	Profile Component 1				Profile Component 2		
	UA	N	A	M	UA	S	D
1							
2							●
3	●		●				
4	●	●					
5	●						
6	●						
7							
8							
9							
10							

N4: Multiplication facts up to 10x10.
A3: Number patterns.
D2: Recording results.

For these four cards there are many possible arrangements, but only 6 possible products:
20, 24, 28, 30, 35, 42

4	6	24
5	7	35

4	5	20
6	7	42

4	7	28
5	6	30

This is usually true for any four cards, except sets such as

| 3 | | 4 | | 6 | | 8 |

. Then, since 3 x 8 = 4 x 6,

there is one less possible product:

3	4	12
6	8	48

3	6	18
4	8	32

3	8	24
4	6	24

In this case, the 5 possible products are:
12, 18, 24, 32, 48

QUESTIONS

(?) How many different arrangements of the 4 cards are there?

(?) Which rows give the smallest/greatest possible products?

(?) What happens if two cards are the same?

EXTENSIONS

(→) Try other sets of 4 cards.

(→) Try choosing from a set of 5 cards.

(→) Try 6 cards in a 3 x 2 arrangement.

Times square

You will need these cards

| 4 | 5 | 6 | 7 |

Place them in a square

4	6
5	7

Multiply together the numbers in each **row**.

4	6	24
5	7	35

Move the cards around in the square and **multiply** again.

go further with
INVESTIGATIONS
SPECTRUM MATHS

13 **Tables**

MULTIPLICATION

NUMBER PATTERNS

Multiplication tables.
Numbers and their factors.
Common multiples.

LEVEL	Profile Component 1				Profile Component 2		
	UA	N	A	M	UA	S	D
1							
2							
3	●		●				●
4	●	●					
5	●		●				
6	●						
7							
8							
9							
10							

N4: Multiplication facts up to 10x10.
A3: Number patterns.
A5: Multiples and factors.
D3: Extracting information from a table.

Pupils can check their tables on a multiplication square.
The multiples are:

x 2	2	4	6	8	10	12	14	16	18	20
x 3	3	6	9	12	15	18	21	24	27	30
x 4	4	8	12	16	20	24	28	32	36	40
x 5	5	10	15	20	25	30	35	40	45	50
x 6	6	12	18	24	30	36	42	48	54	60
x 7	7	14	21	28	35	42	49	56	63	70
x 8	8	16	24	32	40	48	56	64	72	80
x 9	9	18	27	36	45	54	63	72	81	90
x10	10	20	30	40	50	60	70	80	90	100

There are symmetrical patterns along the diagonals.
10 appears as a multiple of 2, 5 and 10.
12 appears as a multiple of 2, 3, 4 and 6.
A table showing the occurrences of particular numbers can be drawn.

Number	Tables			
10	2	5	10	
12	2	3	4	6

QUESTIONS

(?) Which numbers appear many times?

(?) Which numbers appear most times?

(?) Which numbers do not appear at all?

EXTENSIONS

(→) Try multiples of numbers greater than 10.

(→) Try extending the lists beyond the 10th multiple.

(→) Try shading particular numbers on a multiplication square.

Tables

Complete this list of **multiplication tables**.

x 2	2	4	6	8	10	12	14	16	18	20
x 3	3	6	9	12						
x 4	4	8	12	16	20	24				
x 5	5									
x 6	6	12	18							
x 7	7									
x 8			24							
x 9				36						
x 10			30	40						

Can you see any patterns?
How many times does the number 10 appear?

Investigate how many times other numbers appear.

14 Triangle search

TRIANGLES

Drawing different triangles using the diagonals of a regular pentagon as the sides. Isosceles triangles.

Apparatus

Special paper 3 provides regular pentagons.

LEVEL	Profile Component 1				Profile Component 2		
	UA	N	A	M	UA	S	D
1							
2							
3						●	●
4						●	●
5						●	●
6						●	
7							
8							
9							
10							

S3: Sorting triangles and other shapes.
S4: Constructing shapes.
S5: Congruence. Angle properties of triangles.

Pupils need to take care to be accurate when drawing the diagonals and colouring the triangles.
Use a different pentagon for each drawing.
There are five different sized triangles:

    1   2   3   4   5

Several triangles of the same size can be found.

For example, is the same size as number four above.

QUESTIONS

(?) How many triangles of different sizes can you find?

(?) Which is the smallest/largest triangle?

(?) Which triangles are isosceles?

EXTENSIONS

(→) Try finding the same triangle in different positions.

(→) Try exploring four-sided shapes (quadrilaterals).

(→) Try colouring different polygons (3-sided, 4-sided, 5-sided, . . .) inside the pentagons.

(→) Try starting with hexagons.

Triangle search

You will need

pentagon paper

Draw diagonals on a **pentagon**.

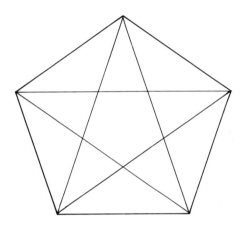

Find a **triangle** and colour it.

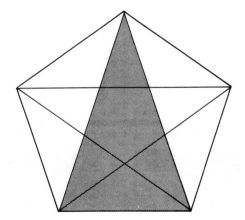

Use other pentagons to find different **triangles**.

15 Stages

SHAPE PATTERNS

Different patterns made by routes on a triangular arrangement of dots.

LEVEL	Profile Component 1				Profile Component 2		
	UA	N	A	M	UA	S	D
1							
2							●
3					●	●	
4					●	●	
5					●		
6					●		
7							
8							
9							
10							

Apparatus

Use special paper 5 for recording.

S3: Sorting shapes (routes) in different ways.
S4: Constructing different shaped routes.
D2: Recording results.

In this investigation, moves like this are not allowed.

One approach is to consider 2-stage routes, then 3-stage routes, and so on.

2 stages

3 stages

4 stages

5 stages

So, there are 10 different routes altogether.

QUESTIONS

(?) How many different 3-stage routes can be found?

(?) Is it possible to find a 6-stage route? Why not?

(?) Which routes touch all the dots?

(?) How many dots does each route touch?

EXTENSIONS

(→) Try starting at a different position, e.g.

(→) Try with 10 dots.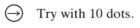

(→) Try allowing this type of move.

Stages

You will need

triangle dotty paper

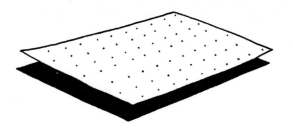

Here are two different **routes** from S to F.

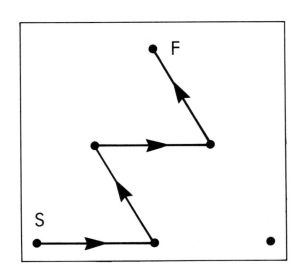

4 **stages**

3 **stages**

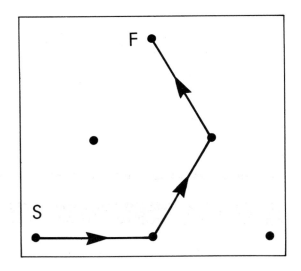

Find some other **routes**.
Dots can be visited only **once**.

Number nine

MIXED NUMBER OPERATIONS

Operations of addition, subtraction, multiplication and division. The need for brackets.

Apparatus

Use number cards 1 to 9. Pupils may use an unlimited number of operation cards.

LEVEL	Profile Component 1				Profile Component 2		
	UA	N	A	M	UA	S	D
1							
2							●
3	●						
4	●	●					
5	●		●				
6	●						
7							
8							
9							
10							

N4: Addition, subtraction, multiplication, division.
A5: Use of brackets.
D2: Recording results.

Pupils should record results after each use of the cards. There is an opportunity here to introduce the need for brackets:

e.g. $\boxed{2}$ $\boxed{1}$ $\boxed{\div}$ $\boxed{7}$ $\boxed{+}$ $\boxed{6}$ can be recorded as $(21 \div 7) + 6$.

One approach is to explore all 3-card expressions first, then 4-card expressions, and so on. Possibilities include:

3 cards: $9 = 1+8, 2+7, 3+6, 4+5, 1 \times 9, 9 \div 1$

4 cards: $9 = 12-3, 13-4, 14-5, 15-6, 16-7, 17-8, 18-9$
$18 \div 2, 27 \div 3, 36 \div 4, 54 \div 6, 63 \div 7, 72 \div 8, 81 \div 9$

5 cards: $9 = 25-16, 35-26, 45-36, 85-76, 95-86, (6 \times 3) \div 2$
$(1+2) \times 3, (7+2) \times 1, (6+3) \times 1, (4+5) \times 1, (2 \times 1)+7, (3 \times 1)+6, (4 \times 1)+5$

6 cards: $9 = (16-5)-2, (17-6)-2, (18-7)-2, (19-8)-2, (9 \times 3)-18, (9 \times 4)-27,$
$(9 \times 5)-36, (56 \div 8)+2, (42 \div 7)+3$

7 cards: $9 = (46-39)+2, (82-76)+3, (8 \times 72) \div 64, (7 \times 81) \div 63, (6 \times 81) \div 54$

8 cards: $9 = (89-67)-13, (79-56)-14, (12 \times 36) \div 48, (12 \times 63) \div 84$

9 cards: $9 = (36-25)+7-9, [(87-65)-9]-4$

QUESTIONS

(?) How many 6-card expressions can you find?

(?) Is it possible to find a 10-card expression, 11-card expression, . . .?

EXTENSIONS

(→) Try limiting expressions to using '+' signs only.

(→) Try for a different target, e.g. 13, 8.

Number nine

You will need
one set of number cards 1 to 9

1 2 3 4 5 6 7 8 9

some operation cards

+ − × ÷

Make **9**. Here are three ways:

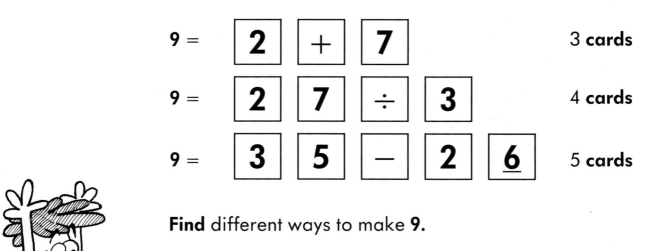

9 = | 2 | + | 7 | 3 **cards**

9 = | 2 | 7 | ÷ | 3 | 4 **cards**

9 = | 3 | 5 | − | 2 | 6 | 5 **cards**

Find different ways to make **9**.

go further with
INVESTIGATIONS
SPECTRUM MATHS

ADDITION

·NUMBER PATTERNS

Patterns in the square arrangements of numbers on a calendar.
Addition of two two-digit numbers.

Apparatus

Use the current month on an up-to-date calendar for more
impact.

LEVEL	Profile Component 1				Profile Component 2		
	UA	N	A	M	UA	S	D
1							
2							
3	●		●				
4	●	●	●				
5	●						
6	●						
7							
8							
9							
10							

N4: Addition of two two-digit numbers.
A3: Explain number patterns.
A4: Generalise patterns in words.

Some examples are:

8	9	10
15	16	17
22	23	24

$8 + 24 = 32$

$10 + 22 = 32$

13	14	15
20	21	22
27	28	29

$13 + 29 = 42$

$27 + 15 = 42$

Generally

a	$a+1$	$a+2$
$a+7$	$a+8$	$a+9$
$a+14$	$a+15$	$a+16$

$a+\underline{a+16} = 2a+16$

$\underline{a+14}+\underline{a+2} = 2a+16$

Note that the sum is 2 x the middle number; i.e.: $[2(a+8)]$.

It is also the sum of
these two numbers

and of these two.

QUESTIONS

(?) What is the sum of opposite corners if the top
left-hand corner number is 9?

(?) What is the sum of opposite corners if the
bottom right-hand corner number is 17?

(?) What is the sum of opposite corners if the
middle number is 10?

EXTENSIONS

(→) Try 2 x 2 squares.

(→) Try 4 x 4 squares.

(→) Try multiplying the opposite corner
numbers together.

(→) Try a different month.

May days

You will need

a calendar

MAY

Sun	Mon	Tues	Wed	Thu	Fri	Sat
	1	2	3	4	5	6
	8	9	10	11	12	13
7	15	16	17	18	19	20
14	22	23	24	25	26	27
21	29	30	31			
28						

Choose a 3 x 3 square on the calendar.

8	9	10
15	16	17
22	23	24

Add opposite corners.

8	
	24

8 + 24 = 32

	10
22	

10 + 22 = 32

Investigate other 3 x 3 squares.

go further with
INVESTIGATIONS
SPECTRUM MATHS

18   **Nets**

CUBES

Finding different nets of 6 squares which will fold to make a cube.

Apparatus

Use card or squared paper to make the nets.

LEVEL	Profile Component 1				Profile Component 2		
	UA	N	A	M	UA	S	D
1							
2							
3					●		
4					●	●	
5					●		
6					●		
7							
8							
9							
10							

S4: Constructing nets for cubes.

There are 11 different nets altogether:

Once the nets have been cut out, they can be checked for duplication by trying to place one on top of the other.

QUESTIONS

(?) How many different nets can be made based on a line of four squares?

(?) What is the surface area of a cube?

(?) How many joins does each net require?

(?) How many faces and edges does a cube have?

EXTENSIONS

(→) Try nets of 5 squares which fold to make open cubes.

(→) Try making nets of a tetrahedron using 4 equilateral triangles.

(→) Try exploring different cubes based on one net and squares of two colours.

Nets

You will need

card

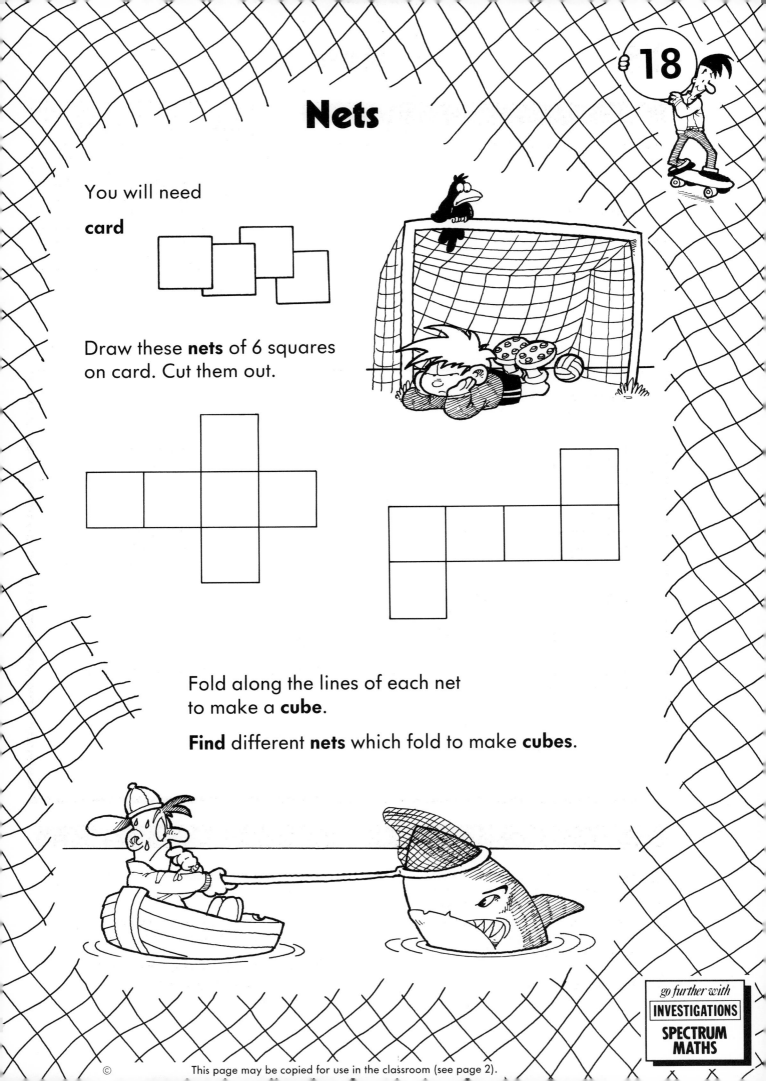

Draw these **nets** of 6 squares
on card. Cut them out.

Fold along the lines of each net
to make a **cube**.

Find different **nets** which fold to make **cubes**.

go further with
INVESTIGATIONS

**SPECTRUM
MATHS**

©   This page may be copied for use in the classroom (see page 2).

19   **Corners**

ADDITION

Addition of one-digit and two-digit numbers.

Patterns associated with 2 x 2 square arrangements of numbers within a 6 x 6 counting square.

Apparatus

Use squared paper to draw the selected 2 x 2 squares.

LEVEL	Profile Component 1				Profile Component 2		
	UA	N	A	M	UA	S	D
1							
2							●
3	●		●				
4	●	●	●				
5	●						
6	●						
7							
8							
9							
10							

N4: Addition of two two-digit numbers.
A3: Number patterns.
A4: Generalise patterns in words.
D2: Recording results.

Pupils should aim to be systematic by considering squares in some sort of sequence. For example, they could move along the top two rows, then the second and third rows, and so on.

The different totals are:

9	11	13	15	17
21	23	25	27	29
33	35	37	39	41
45	47	49	51	53
57	59	61	63	65

There are 25 different possible totals — all the odd numbers between 9 and 65 inclusive, except 19, 31, 43, 55.

If 3 x 3 squares are considered, the corner totals are as shown here.

16	18	20	22
28	30	32	34
40	42	44	46
52	54	56	58

There are 16 different totals — all the even numbers between 16 and 58 inclusive, except 24, 26, 36, 38, 48, 50.

QUESTIONS

(?) Which square gives a corner total of 23?

(?) What is the smallest/greatest corner total?

(?) How many different totals are possible?

EXTENSIONS

(→) Try 3 x 3 squares, then 4 x 4 squares.

(→) Try adding all four corner numbers.

(→) Try with a different sized original grid.

Corners

You will need

squared paper

1	2	3	4	5	6
7	8	9	10	11	12
13	14	15	16	17	18
19	20	21	22	23	24
25	26	27	28	29	30
31	32	33	34	35	36

Choose some **2 x 2 squares** from this grid.
Draw them and then **add opposite corners**.

4	5
10	11

$4 + 11 = \textbf{15}$

15	16
21	22

$15 + 22 = \textbf{37}$

Investigate other **2 x 2 squares**.

Nearest wholes

DECIMALS

Choosing two digits from three to make different decimal numbers of this form: □·□

Finding the nearest whole number to each decimal number.

Apparatus

Use cards numbered 1 to 9.

LEVEL	Profile Component 1				Profile Component 2		
	UA	N	A	M	UA	S	D
1							
2							
3	●						
4	●						
5	●						
6	●	●					
7							
8							
9							
10							

N6: Approximate decimal numbers to nearest whole number.

There are six different arrangements of two cards.

nearest
whole number

4·7	⟶	5
7·4	⟶	7
3·4	⟶	3
4·3	⟶	4
3·7	⟶	4
7·3	⟶	7

There are four different nearest whole numbers: 3, 4, 5, 7.

The use of a number line may be helpful to clarify the idea of nearest.

```
3                    4                    5
└─┴─┴─┴─┴─┴─┴─┴─┴─┴─┴─┴─┴─┴─┴─┴─┴─┴─┴─┴─┘
```

QUESTIONS

(?) What is the nearest whole number to 3·4, 4·7?

(?) Which of the decimal numbers are nearest to 7?

(?) Which of the decimal numbers are between 3 and 4?

EXTENSIONS

(→) Try with a different set of 3 cards.

(→) Try to make more than four different nearest whole numbers.

(→) Try with a different arrangement, e.g. □□·□

(→) Try with four cards.

Nearest wholes

You will need these cards

| 3 | 4 | 7 |

Choose two cards and place them in these spaces to make a **decimal number.**

☐ • ☐

Find the **nearest whole number.**

Examples

7 · 3 nearest ⟶ 7

4 · 7 ⟶ 5

How many different decimal numbers and **nearest whole numbers** can you find?

Equations

MIXED NUMBER OPERATIONS

Making equations involving addition, subtraction, multiplication, division, and combinations of these. Rearrangements of equations.

Apparatus

Use number cards 1 to 9, and operation cards +, x, −, ÷.

LEVEL	Profile Component 1				Profile Component 2		
	UA	N	A	M	UA	S	D
1							
2							●
3	●						
4	●	●	●				
5	●						
6	●						
7							
8							
9							
10							

N4: Mixed number operations.
A4: Simple equations.
D2: Recording results.

Many equations are possible:

Using + only.

$7 = 5+2$
$12 = 5+7$
$14 = 5+7+2$
$5 = 1+4$
$7 = 1+4+2$

Using − only.

$5-1 = 4$
$5-4 = 1$
$7-5 = 2$
$7-2 = 5$
$12-5 = 7$
$12-7 = 5$
$(14-5)-7 = 2$
$(7-4)-2 = 1$

Using ÷ only.

$14÷7 = 2$
$14÷2 = 7$

Using + and − .

$4+2 = 7-1$
$7+2 = 14-5$
$5+2 = 14-7$
$5+7 = 14-2$
$4+1 = 7-2$
$1+2 = 7-4$

Using various combinations.

$14 = 7×2$
$7+1 = 4×2$
$7-5 = 4÷2$
$4 = (7+1)÷2$

QUESTIONS

(?) How many different equations can be found using + only?

(?) How many ways are there of rearranging $7 = 5 + 2$?

(?) How many different equations can be found using all 5 cards?

EXTENSIONS

(→) Try with [1] [2] [3] [5] [8].

(→) Try with six cards.

(→) Try making different expressions using [1] [4] [2] [7] [5], e.g. 16 = [1] [4] [+] [2], 17 = [1] [2] [+] [5], and so on.

You will need

these number cards

| 1 | 4 | 2 | 7 | 5 |

some operation cards

| + | + | − | × | ÷ |

Make **equations**.

| 1 | 4 | = | 7 | × | 2 |

| 7 | = | 5 | + | 2 |

Make as many different **equations** as you can.

AREA

PERIMETER

Exploration of the area and perimeter of different shapes. Shapes with a constant area and differing perimeters. Shapes with a constant perimeter and differing areas.

Apparatus

Squares are necessary to find different shapes. Use squared paper for recording.

LEVEL	Profile Component 1				Profile Component 2		
	UA	N	A	M	UA	S	D
1							
2						●	●
3	●			●	●		
4	●			●	●		
5	●				●		
6	●				●		
7							
8							
9							
10							

M3: Perimeter.
M4: Area by counting squares.
S2: Creating shapes using squares.
D2: Recording shapes.

Pupils might explore shapes with:

(a) different perimeters and the same area.

P = 12
A = 8

P = 14
A = 8

P = 16
A = 8

P = 18
A = 8

(b) different areas and the same perimeter.

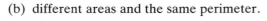

P = 12
A = 5

P = 12
A = 8

P = 12
A = 8

P = 12
A = 6

P = 12
A = 7

P = 12
A = 9

QUESTIONS

(?) Is it possible to have a perimeter of an odd number of units?

(?) Can you make a shape with perimeter 8 units and area 4 square units?

(?) Can you make a shape with perimeter 16 units and area 16 square units?

(?) What is the smallest/largest possible perimeter for a shape of area 9 square units.

EXTENSIONS

(→) Try exploring the different possible perimeters of 6-square shapes.

(→) Try introducing right-angled triangles to make shapes of this type.

A = 2
P = 4+2 diagonals.

Double measures

You will need

squares
squared paper

Use **squares** to make shapes

Area : 3 square units
Perimeter : 8 units

Area : 8 square units
Perimeter : 12 units

Make some more **shapes**.
Find the **area** and **perimeter** of each.

go further with
INVESTIGATIONS

SPECTRUM MATHS

Quadrilaterals

POLYGONS

Finding different quadrilaterals on a 3 x 3 geoboard. Naming quadrilaterals: square, rectangle, parallelogram, trapezium.

Apparatus

Use the geoboards to explore the different shapes and special paper 4 for recording the quadrilaterals.

LEVEL	Profile Component 1				Profile Component 2		
	UA	N	A	M	UA	S	D
1							
2							●
3					●	●	
4				●	●	●	
5					●		
6					●	●	
7							
8							
9							
10							

M4: Areas of polygons.
S3: Sorting shapes in different ways.
S4: Constructing shapes.
S6: Classifying types of quadrilaterals.
D2: Recording shapes.

There are 16 different quadrilaterals:

Some of the quadrilaterals can be labelled: square, rectangle, etc.

QUESTIONS

(?) How many different squares are there?

(?) What are the names of the quadrilaterals?

(?) What is the area of each quadrilateral?

(?) Which are symmetrical?

EXTENSIONS

(→) Try pentagons.

(→) Try quadrilaterals on a 3 x 4 board.

(→) Try finding the same quadrilateral in different positions.

(→) Try exploring the perimeters of the quadrilaterals.

Quadrilaterals

You will need

**square dotty paper
a 3 x 3 geoboard
an elastic band**

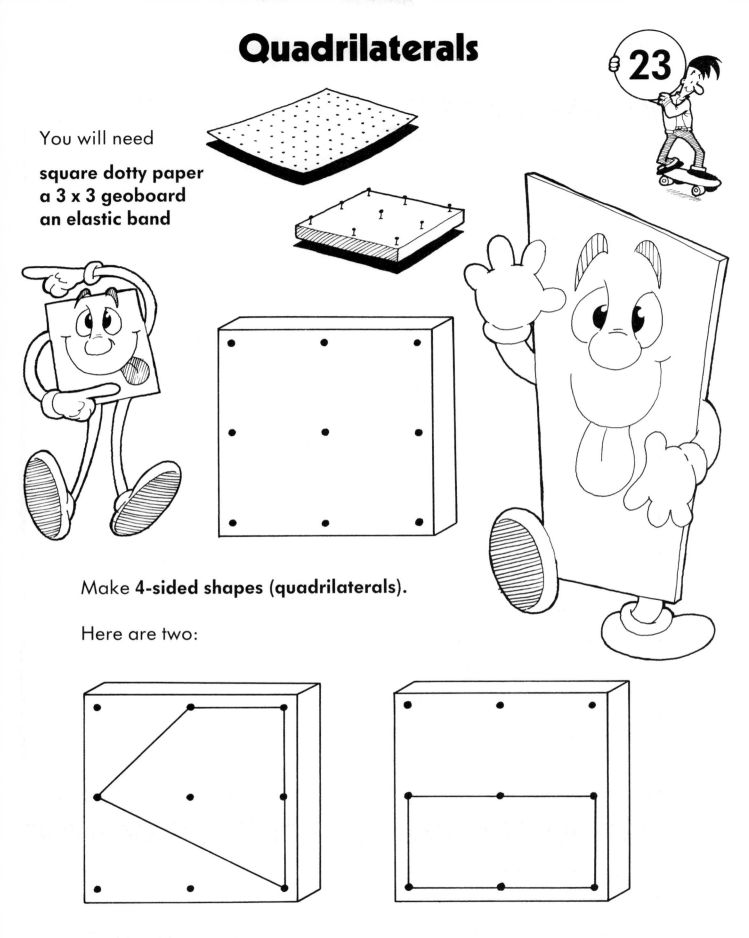

Make **4-sided shapes (quadrilaterals).**

Here are two:

How many different **quadrilaterals**
can you make?

24 Production lines

NUMBER PATTERNS

Patterns formed by finding the digital products of all numbers up to 100 on a 1 to 100 counting square.

Apparatus

Squared paper is needed for drawing a 10 x 10 square for recording.

LEVEL	Profile Component 1				Profile Component 2		
	UA	N	A	M	UA	S	D
1							
2							
3	●		●				
4	●	●					
5	●						
6	●						
7							
8							
9							
10							

N4: Multiplication facts up to 10x10.
A3: Number patterns.

The digital products are:

Note the symmetry in some of the diagonal patterns, e.g.:

```
            8
        0       4
      8           6
     8           5
   0           8
  8         5
       6
     4
```

1	2	3	4	5	6	7	8	9	0
1	2	3	4	5	6	7	8	9	0
2	4	6	8	0	2	4	6	8	0
3	6	9	2	5	8	2	8	4	0
4	8	2	6	0	8	6	6	8	0
5	0	5	0	0	0	5	0	0	0
6	2	8	8	0	8	8	6	0	0
7	4	2	6	5	8	8	0	8	0
8	6	8	6	0	6	0	8	4	0
9	8	4	8	0	0	8	4	8	0

line of symmetry

QUESTIONS

(?) What do you notice about the last column?

(?) What do you notice about the digital products of the 50s?

(?) Which numbers appear least/most often as digital products?

EXTENSIONS

(→) Try extending to 3-digit numbers on the counting square.

(→) Try exploring the digital products on a multiplication square.

(→) Try exploring the last digit of the product of the digits for example, 47 → 8 (4 x 7 = 28, and the last digit is 8).

Production lines

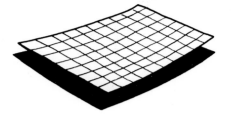

1	2	3	4	5	6	7	8	9	10
11	12	13	14	15	16	17	18	19	20
21	22	23	24	25	26	27	28	29	30
31	32	33	34	35	36	37	38	39	40
41	42	43	44	45	46	47	48	49	50
51	52	53	54	55	56	57	58	59	60
61	62	63	64	65	66	67	68	69	70
71	72	73	74	75	76	77	78	79	80
81	82	83	84	85	86	87	88	89	90
91	92	93	94	95	96	97	98	99	100

You will need

squared paper

Start with a 1 to 100 square.

The **digital product** of
24 is **8** (2 x 4 = **8**)
47 is **6** (4 x 7 = 28, then 2 x 8 = 16, then 1 x 6 = **6**)

Draw a blank
10 x 10 square.
Write in the
digital products.

Fill in the whole square.

8

6

Find patterns.

DIVISION

Finding different possible division statements using digits chosen from the set 0 to 9 (no repeats allowed).

Apparatus

Use one set of number cards 0 to 9, and just one operation card for ÷.

LEVEL	Profile Component 1				Profile Component 2		
	UA	N	A	M	UA	S	D
1							
2							●
3	●		●				
4	●	●					
5	●						
6	●						
7							
8							
9							
10							

N4: Dividing a 2-digit number by a single-digit number.
A3: Number patterns.
D2: Recording results.

Many different division sentences are possible:

$6 \div 3 = 2$ $8 \div 4 = 2$ $10 \div 5 = 2$ $18 \div 6 = 3$ $14 \div 7 = 2$ $16 \div 8 = 2$ $18 \div 9 = 2$

           $12 \div 4 = 3$ $20 \div 5 = 4$ $30 \div 6 = 5$ $21 \div 7 = 3$ $24 \div 8 = 3$ $27 \div 9 = 3$

                                      $28 \div 7 = 4$ $32 \div 8 = 4$ $36 \div 9 = 4$

                                      $42 \div 7 = 6$ $40 \div 8 = 5$ $54 \div 9 = 6$

                                                   $56 \div 8 = 7$ $63 \div 9 = 7$

                                                                $72 \div 9 = 8$

Each of these can be expressed in two ways.

For example, $8 \div 4 = 2$ and $8 \div 2 = 4$.

Pupils may find calculators helpful.

QUESTIONS

(?) How many sentences can be found to equal 2?

(?) Can you find two different sentences with the result 18?

EXTENSIONS

(→) Try making sentences with two-digit results, e.g. $60 \div 5 = 12$.

(→) Try replacing ÷ by ×.

(→) Try finding all the different sentences that include a 5.

Divisions

You will need

one set of cards for 0 to 9

| 0 | 1 | 2 | 3 | 4 |

| 5 | 6 | 7 | 8 | 9 |

a division operation card $\div$

Make **division** sentences like these:

$$6\ 3 \div 7 = 9$$

$$1\ 2 \div 4 = 3$$

Find different **division** sentences.

SHAPE PATTERNS

Finding different shapes by arranging four L-shaped pieces.

Apparatus

Pupils will need four L-shaped pieces.
These can be made by cutting one quarter from each of four card squares.

LEVEL	Profile Component 1				Profile Component 2		
	UA	N	A	M	UA	S	D
1							
2						●	●
3					●	●	
4					●	●	
5					●		
6					●		
7							
8							
9							
10							

S2: Creating pictures using 2D shapes.
S3: Symmetry.
S4: Constructing shapes: rectangles etc.
D2: Recording shapes.

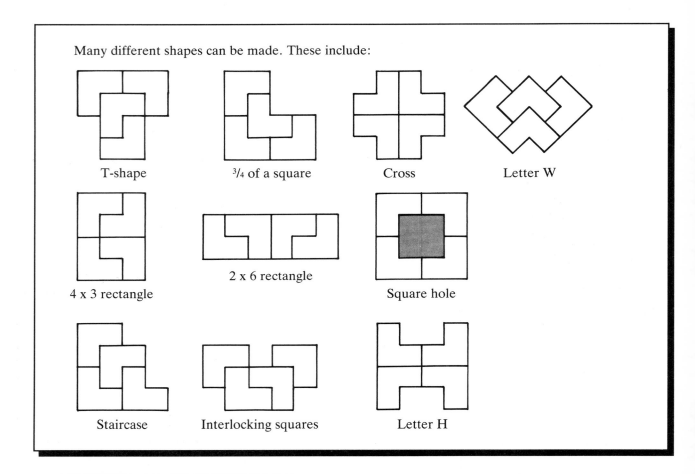

Many different shapes can be made. These include:

T-shape   ³/₄ of a square   Cross   Letter W

4 x 3 rectangle   2 x 6 rectangle   Square hole

Staircase   Interlocking squares   Letter H

QUESTIONS

(?) What is the area in square units of one L-piece?

(?) What is the area in square units of each shape?

(?) How many rectangles of different sizes can be made?

EXTENSIONS

(→) Try exploring the perimeters of the different shapes.

(→) Try making symmetrical shapes.

(→) Try making shapes using four of these:

Foursomes

You will need

card squares

Start with 4 **squares**.

Make four of these shapes by cutting one quarter out of each square.

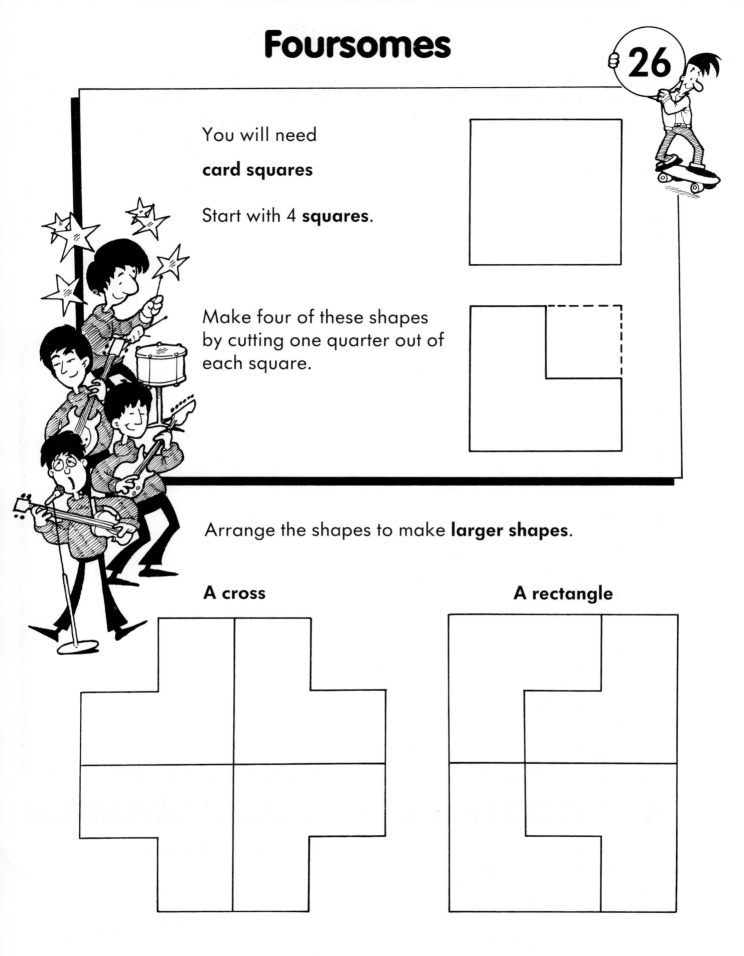

Arrange the shapes to make **larger shapes**.

A cross

A rectangle

Make other **shapes**.

AREA

Drawing different sized squares on square dotty paper and finding the area of each.

Apparatus

Special paper 4 can be used for recording the different squares. Geoboards can be used for finding the squares.

LEVEL	Profile Component 1				Profile Component 2		
	UA	N	A	M	UA	S	D
1							
2							
3	●						
4	●			●		●	
5	●						
6	●						
7							
8							
9							
10							

M4: Area by counting squares.
S4: Constructing shapes.

If any two dots are joined by a straight line then it is possible to draw a square with that line as an edge.
For example:

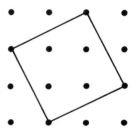

Area 5 square units

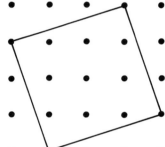

Area 10 square units

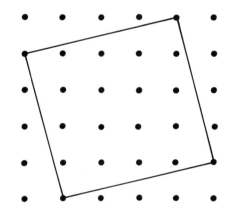

Area 17 square units

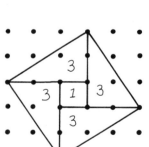

Area 13 square units

The areas can be found by dividing the squares into sections.
It is possible to draw squares with the following areas:
1, 2, 4, 5, 8, 9, 10, 13, 16, 17, 18, 20, . . . square units.

QUESTIONS

(?) What square areas of less than 6 square units can be found?

(?) What square areas are not possible?

(?) What are the areas of squares drawn with horizontal and vertical lines?

EXTENSIONS

(→) Try drawing triangles with different areas.

(→) Try drawing rectangles.

Dotty squares

You will need

square dotty paper

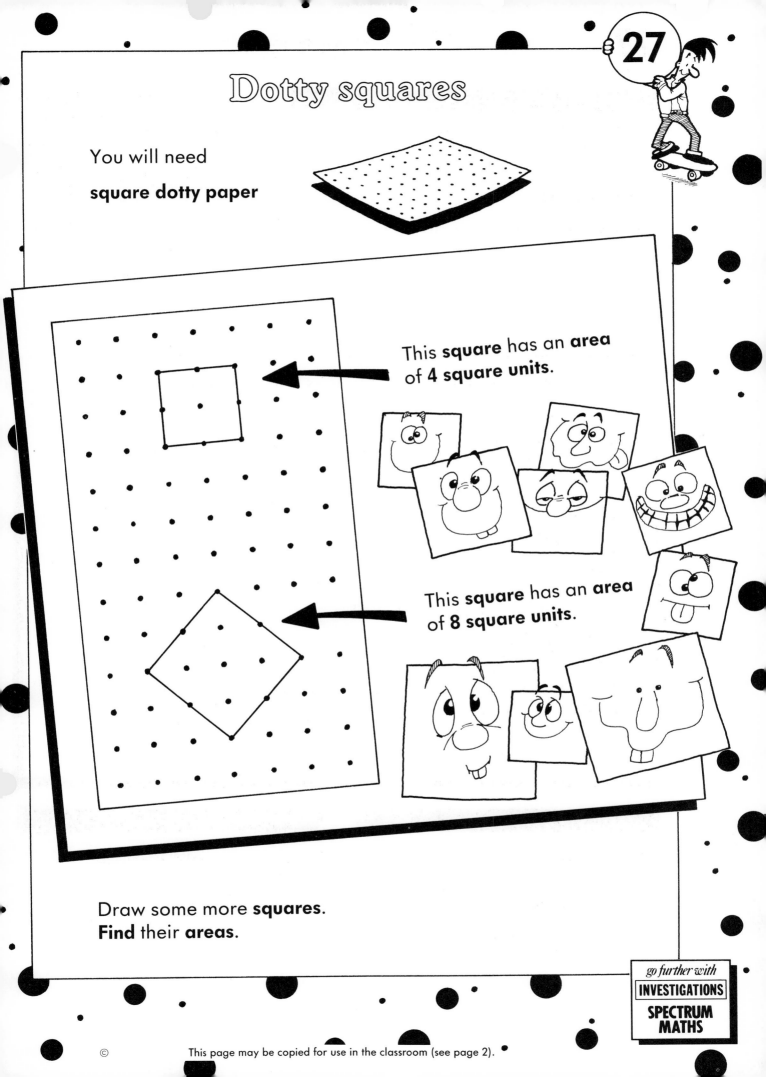

This **square** has an **area** of **4 square units**.

This **square** has an **area** of **8 square units**.

Draw some more **squares**.
Find their **areas**.

Trails

ADDITION

Addition of several single-digit numbers.
Different paths across a 3 x 3 grid.

Apparatus

Use squared paper to record the different trails across the grid.

LEVEL	Profile Component 1				Profile Component 2		
	UA	N	A	M	UA	S	D
1							
2							●
3					●	●	
4		●			●		
5					●	●	
6					●		
7							
8							
9							
10							

N4: Addition of several single-digit numbers.
S3: Sorting shapes.
S5: Traversing networks.
D2: Recording results.

Assume that a diagonal move is not allowed. Then, if the first move is upward:

    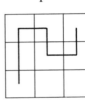 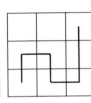

$2 + 6 + 9 + 5$ $+ 4 = 26$	$2 + 6 + 7 + 8$ $+ 4 = 27$	$2 + 6 + 7 + 5$ $+ 4 = 24$	$2 + 6 + 9 + 5$ $+ 7 + 3 + 1$ $+ 8 + 4 = 45$	$2 + 6 + 9 +$ $5 + 7 + 8 +$ $4 = 41$	$2 + 6 + 7 +$ $3 + 1 + 8 +$ $4 = 31$

And if the first move is across:

   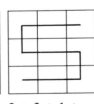 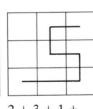 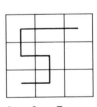

$2 + 3 + 1 +$ $8 + 4 = 18$	$2 + 3 + 7 +$ $5 + 4 = 21$	$2 + 3 + 7 +$ $8 + 4 = 24$	$2 + 3 + 1 +$ $8 + 7 + 6 +$ $9 + 5 +$ $4 = 45$	$2 + 3 + 1 +$ $8 + 7 + 5 +$ $4 = 30$	$2 + 3 + 7 +$ $6 + 9 + 5 +$ $4 = 36$

There are 12 possible trails producing 10 different totals:
18, 21, 24, 26, 27, 30, 31, 36, 41, 45

QUESTIONS

(?) How many different trails can you find?

(?) Which trail gives the smallest/greatest total?

(?) Which trails have a total nearest to 25?

EXTENSIONS

(→) Try exploring longer trails.

(→) Try with a different arrangement of the numbers.

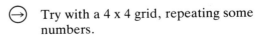

(→) Try with a 4 x 4 grid, repeating some numbers.

(→) Try with a rectangular grid.

Trails

You will need

squared paper

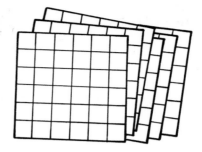

Draw this.

9	5	4
6	7	8
2	3	1

Finish

Start

Draw a **trail** from start to finish.

9	5	4
6	7→	8
2→	3	1

Finish

Start

This trail is: 2 + 3 + 7 + 8 + 4 = **24**.

Find other **trails**.

MULTIPLICATION

NUMBER PATTERNS

Patterns in the results of multiplying two-digit numbers by 11.

Apparatus

Calculators are suggested for multiplying by 11, though pupils could also try to use a multiplication algorithm.

LEVEL	Profile Component 1				Profile Component 2		
	UA	N	A	M	UA	S	D
1							
2							
3	●						
4	●	●	●				
5	●						
6	●						
7							
8							
9							
10							

N4: Multiplication of two-digit numbers by 11.
A4: Generalising patterns in words.

Pupils should eventually be encouraged to predict the answer, and then use the calculator as a check.

To start with, pupils could list some numbers in order and multiply them by 11. For example:

$$21 \times 11 = 231$$
$$22 \times 11 = 242$$
$$23 \times 11 = 253$$
$$24 \times 11 = 264$$
$$25 \times 11 = 275$$
$$26 \times 11 = 286$$
$$27 \times 11 = 297$$
$$28 \times 11 = 308$$
$$29 \times 11 = 319$$

A pattern emerges here:

$$ab \times 11 = a \; a{+}b \; b$$
e.g. $21 \times 11 = 2 \; 2{+}1 \; 1$
        $21 \times 11 = 2 \;\; 3 \;\; 1$

The pattern needs adapting slightly here.

11	12	13	14	15	16	17	18
21	22	23	24	25	26	27	
31	32	33	34	35	36		
41	42	43	44	45			
51	52	53	54				
61	62	63					
71	72						
81							

Numbers which can be most easily multiplied by 11 'in the head' are those whose digit sum is not more than 9.

QUESTIONS

(?) Can you multiply these by 11, 'in your head'
   − 31, 43, 62?

(?) How far can you go with the 11-times table?

(?) How many two-digit numbers have a digital sum not more than 9?

EXTENSIONS

(→) Try multiplying three-digit numbers by 11.

(→) Try multiplying by 101, 111, . . .

Elevenses

You will need

a calculator

$$23 \times \mathbf{11} = 253$$
$$42 \times \mathbf{11} = 462$$

Multiply some more numbers by **11**.
Search for **patterns**.

Look for a **quick method** that does not
use a calculator.

go further with
INVESTIGATIONS
SPECTRUM MATHS

©   This page may be copied for use in the classroom (see page 2).

30 Tri-hard

POLYGONS

Joining right-angled isosceles triangles to make different shapes. Names of different polygons. Perimeter. Conservation of area.

Apparatus

Triangles can be cut from squares of card. Use squared paper for recording the different shapes.

LEVEL	Profile Component 1				Profile Component 2		
	UA	N	A	M	UA	S	D
1							
2							●
3				●	●	●	
4					●	●	
5					●		
6					●		
7							
8							
9							
10							

M3: Perimeter.
S3: Sorting shapes.
S4: Constructing different shapes from right-angled triangles.
D2: Recording results.

There are 4 different possible shapes using 3 right-angled triangles.

There are 14 different possible shapes using 4 right-angled triangles.

QUESTIONS

(?) Which shapes have the same area?

(?) What are the names of the three two-triangle shapes?

(?) Can you name some of the other shapes?

(?) How many sides does each shape have?

EXTENSIONS

(→) Try exploring the perimeters of the shapes in terms of square edges and diagonals, e.g. ⊠ – 2 edges + 3 diagonals.

(→) Try joining equilateral triangles.

Tri-hard

You will need

card squares
squared paper

Start with a square.

Make two triangles by cutting the square in half, like this.

Join the pieces to make shapes.

Cut another square in half.
Use three triangles to make shapes.

Square search

SQUARES

NUMBER PATTERNS

Counting the different squares in rectangular grids. Patterns in the numbers of squares of different sizes.

Apparatus

Use squared paper for recording the different rectangles and illustrating their division into different squares.

LEVEL	Profile Component 1				Profile Component 2		
	UA	N	A	M	UA	S	D
1							
2						●	
3	●		●				
4	●		●				
5	●						
6	●						
7							
8							
9							
10							

A3: Explaining number patterns.
A4: Generalising patterns in words.
S2: Rectangles.

Discussion may be necessary to establish that a square is a special rectangle. So, for instance, a 3 x 3 square grid can be considered.
The squares can be illustrated by coloured outlines.

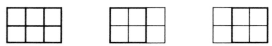

A systematic approach is to consider first the rectangles of width 2, then of width 3.

Rectangle	1x1 squares	2x2 squares	3x3 squares	
2x3	6	2		8
2x4	8	3		11
2x5	10	4		14
: :				
2xb	$2b$	$b-1$		$2b+b-1$ or $3b-1$
3x2	6	2		8
3x3	9	4	1	14
3x4	12	6	2	20
: :				
3xb	$3b$	$2(b-1)$	$b-2$	$6b-4$

QUESTIONS

(?) How many squares are there in a 5 x 1, 7 x 1, 10 x 1, . . . rectangle?

(?) How many 1 x 1 squares are there in a 5 x 3 rectangle?

(?) What is the area of each rectangle?

(?) What is the largest possible square in a 10 x 3 rectangle?

EXTENSIONS

(→) Try exploring the number of rectangles in a rectangular grid.

(→) Try exploring the number of triangles in a triangular grid.

Square search

You will need
squared paper

This is a **2 x 3 rectangle**.

It has **6 squares**.
Find them.

How many **squares** are there
in this **2 x 4 rectangle**?

Find how many **squares** there are
in other **rectangles**.

©

Total amazements

ADDITION

Addition of two, three, four, . . . numbers to make given totals.

Different ways of summing four numbers, for example, to make a given total.

Apparatus

Use cards numbered 1 to 20.

LEVEL	Profile Component 1				Profile Component 2		
	UA	N	A	M	UA	S	D
1							
2							●
3	●		●				
4	●	●					
5	●						
6	●						
7							
8							
9							
10							

N4: Addition of several single-digit numbers.
A3: Number patterns.
D2: Recording results.

One approach is to list all the possible ways of making the total 15 using 2 cards, 3 cards, and so on.

2 cards	3 cards	4 cards	5 cards
1 14	1 2 12	1 2 3 9	1 2 3 4 5
2 13	1 3 11	1 2 4 8	
3 12	1 4 10	1 2 5 7	
4 11	1 5 9		
5 10	1 6 8	1 3 4 7	
6 9		1 3 5 6	
7 8	2 3 10		
	2 4 9	2 3 4 6	
	2 5 8		
	2 6 7		
	3 4 8		
	3 5 7		
	4 5 6		

So possible solutions include:

| 6 | 9 | 2 cards
| 1 | 2 | 3 | 4 | 5 | 5 cards

| 7 | 8 | 2 cards
| 2 | 4 | 9 | 3 cards
| 1 | 3 | 5 | 6 | 4 cards

QUESTIONS

(?) How many different 2-card totals of 15 are possible?

(?) Is it possible to find a 5-card total of 15?

(?) Is it possible to find a 5-card total of 14?

(?) How many different 4-card totals of 12 can you find?

EXTENSIONS

(→) Try different totals.

(→) Try using different cards, e.g. 5 to 25.

Total amazements

You will need

cards 1 to 20

1	2	3	4	5	6	7	8	9	10
11	12	13	14	15	16	17	18	19	20

Choose a **total**. ➡ **20**

Now make the **total 20** in different ways.

Each card may only be used **once**.

| 9 | 11 | | | **2 cards** |

| 5 | 7 | 8 | | **3 cards** |

| 10 | 6 | 3 | 1 | **4 cards** |

Start again and make the **total 15**
in different ways.

Make some **totals** of your own.

33   **Signs**

MIXED NUMBER OPERATIONS

Operations of addition, subtraction and multiplication.
Combinations of two operations. The need for brackets.

Apparatus

Calculators may be useful for checking some of the harder
expressions.

LEVEL	Profile Component 1				Profile Component 2		
	UA	N	A	M	UA	S	D
1							
2							
3			●				
4		●					
5							
6							
7							
8							
9							
10							

N4: Addition, subtraction, multiplication
involving single-digit, two-digit and
three-digit numbers.
A3: Number patterns.

Some possibilities are:

Using '+' signs
$32 = 23 + 9$
$41 = 32 + 9$
$32 = 29 + 3$
$95 = 92 + 3$
$41 = 39 + 2$
$95 = 93 + 2$
$14 = 2 + 3 + 9$

Using '–' signs
$14 = 23 - 9$
$23 = 32 - 9$
$26 = 29 - 3$
$89 = 92 - 3$
$37 = 39 - 2$
$91 = 93 - 2$
$4 = (9-3) - 2$
$8 = 9 - (3-2)$

Using 'x' signs
$207 = 23 \times 9$
$288 = 32 \times 9$
$276 = 92 \times 3$
$87 = 29 \times 3$
$78 = 39 \times 2$
$186 = 93 \times 2$
$54 = 2 \times 3 \times 9$

Using '+' or '–' and 'x' signs
$29 = (3 \times 9) + 2$
$25 = (3 \times 9) - 2$
$21 = (2 \times 9) + 3$
$15 = (2 \times 9) - 3$
$15 = (2 \times 3) + 9$
$3 = 9 - (2 \times 3)$

QUESTIONS

(?)   Which numbers have more than one different
expression? e.g. $32 = 23 + 9$, $32 = 29 + 3$.

(?)   Which is the greatest possible number?

EXTENSIONS

(→)   Try with a different set of digits.

(→)   Try using division signs, e.g.
$5 = (9 \div 3) + 2$.

(→)   Try using power signs, e.g.
$18 = 3^2 + 9$.

(→)   Try using square root signs, e.g.
$16 = \sqrt{9} + 13$.

Signs

You will need

a calculator

Use the digits **9**, **3** and **2** to make **numbers**.
A digit may only be used **once** each time.

Here are some examples.

Using '+' signs
39 + 2 makes **41**
92 + 3 makes **95**

Using '−' signs
39 − 2 makes **37**
(9−3) − 2 makes **4**

Using '+' or '−' and 'x' signs
(3 x 9) + 2 makes **29**
(2 x 9) − 3 makes **15**

Make some more **numbers** using 9, 3 and 2.

34 Regions

SHAPE PATTERNS

Investigating the number of regions formed by chords joining different numbers of points marked on the circumference of circles.

Apparatus

The circles can be drawn with compasses, or by drawing around a circle template.

LEVEL	Profile Component 1				Profile Component 2		
	UA	N	A	M	UA	S	D
1							
2							
3	●		●				
4	●						●
5	●						
6	●						
7							
8							
9							
10							

A3: Searching for number patterns.
S4: Constructing shapes and their diagonals.

Pupils should draw large circles, particularly when using more than 4 dots, so that they can easily count the regions.

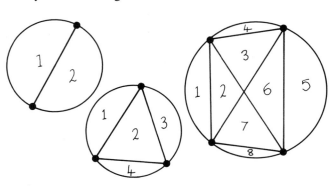

A pattern appears to be emerging for 2, 3, 4 and 5 dots, but it breaks down with 6 dots.

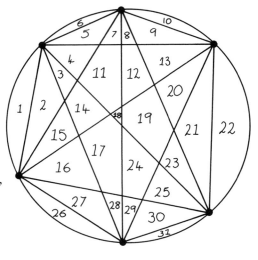

Number of dots	Number of regions
2	2
3	4
4	8
5	16
6	31

Note: For a regular hexagon this figure is 30, because region 18, above, disappears.

QUESTIONS

(?) What shapes are the regions?

(?) How many of the regions are triangles?

(?) How many chords are drawn from each dot?

EXTENSIONS

(→) Try counting the number of intersections.

(→) Try counting the number of straight lines.

Regions

You will need

circles

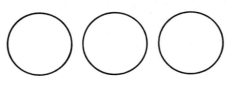

Draw a circle.
Mark 4 dots.
Join them with straight lines.

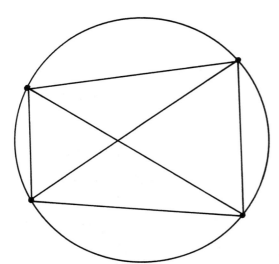

Count the number of **regions**.
There are **8**

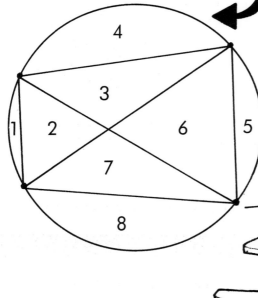

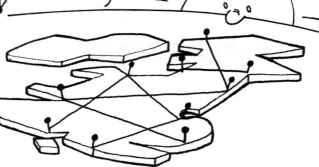

Draw another circle.
Change the number of dots.
Count the number of **regions**.

go further with
INVESTIGATIONS
SPECTRUM MATHS

35 **Perimeter dots**

TRIANGLES

Exploration of different triangles measured in terms of
'perimeter' dots and 'inside' dots. Types of
triangle: equilateral, isosceles, acute-angled, obtuse-angled,
right-angled.

Apparatus

Use special paper 5 to find and record the triangles. Pupils
may want to cut out their triangles when recording.

LEVEL	Profile Component 1				Profile Component 2		
	UA	N	A	M	UA	S	D
1							
2							●
3					●	●	
4					●	●	
5					●		
6					●		
7							
8							
9							
10							

S3: Sorting triangles.
S4: Constructing different triangles.
D2: Recording shapes.

One approach is to fix the number of perimeter dots on one side and then search for different
positions for the other two sides. In this example, one side with 5 dots is fixed:

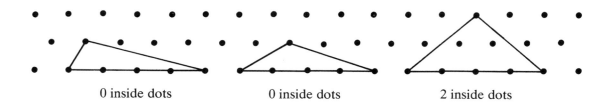

| 0 inside dots | 0 inside dots | 2 inside dots |

Here, one side with 4 dots is fixed:

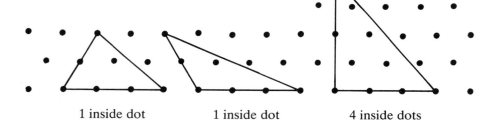

| 1 inside dot | 1 inside dot | 4 inside dots |

QUESTIONS

(?) Which triangles are equilateral?

(?) Which triangles are isosceles?

(?) Which triangles are right-angled?

(?) Is it possible to make a triangle with 2 inside
dots, 3 inside dots, . . .?

EXTENSIONS

(→) Try drawing different triangles with
2 inside dots.

(→) Try drawing triangles on square
dotty paper.

Perimeter dots

You will need

triangle dotty paper

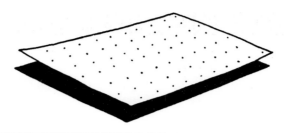

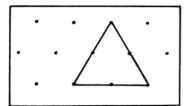

0 inside dots

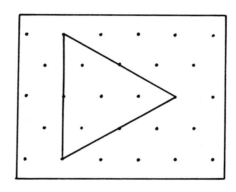

4 inside dots

2 inside dots

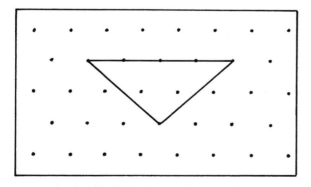

Each of these **triangles** has **6 perimeter dots**.

Find some more **triangles** with **6 perimeter dots**.

go further with
INVESTIGATIONS
SPECTRUM MATHS

MULTIPLICATION

Multiplication of two-digit numbers. Commutativity.
Estimation.

Apparatus

Use number cards 1 to 9. These will help pupils to search for
different arrangements. The calculators can be used to
perform the multiplications.

LEVEL	Profile Component 1				Profile Component 2		
	UA	N	A	M	UA	S	D
1							
2							●
3	●						
4	●	●					
5	●						
6	●						
7							
8							
9							
10							

N4: Multiplication of two two-digit numbers.
D2: Recording results.

Pupils should be encouraged to estimate an answer before using the calculator. Some
discussion is useful about $34 \atop \times 56$ and $56 \atop \times 34$ having the same value, i.e. commutativity.

A systematic approach is to try all possible arrangements with the 3 as a tens digit, and then all
the possible arrangements with the 3 as a units digit.

The different possibilities are:

$35 \atop \times 46$	$35 \atop \times 64$	$34 \atop \times 56$	$34 \atop \times 65$	$36 \atop \times 54$	$36 \atop \times 45$
1610	2240	1904	2210	1944	1620

$53 \atop \times 46$	$53 \atop \times 64$	$63 \atop \times 45$	$63 \atop \times 54$	$43 \atop \times 56$	$43 \atop \times 65$
2438	3392	2835	3402	2408	2795

So there are 12 different possible answers altogether.

QUESTIONS

(?) What is the smallest/greatest possible answer?

(?) How many answers end in zero?

(?) Is it possible to predict the end digits in the
answers?

(?) Will there always be 12 different answers?

EXTENSIONS

(→) Try with a different set of 4 cards.

(→) Try with two cards the same, e.g.
[2] [2] [3] [5] .

(→) Try with two three-digit numbers and 6 cards.

Hard times

You will need

a calculator
these cards

| 3 | 5 | 4 | 6 |

Arrange the cards as a
multiplication calculation.

×	

Find the answer by using a calculator.

Examples

3	5
× 4	6

1 6 1 0

5	4
× 3	6

1 9 4 4

Investigate different **answers**.

go further with
INVESTIGATIONS
SPECTRUM MATHS

37 Multiples

MULTIPLICATION

Multiples of different numbers, possibly extending beyond the tenth multiple. Odds, evens, square and prime numbers.

Apparatus

Use cards numbered 0 to 9.

LEVEL	Profile Component 1				Profile Component 2		
	UA	N	A	M	UA	S	D
1							
2							●
3	●						
4	●						
5	●		●				
6	●						
7							
8							
9							
10							

A5: Multiples of single-digit numbers. Primes and square numbers.
D2: Recording results.

Pupils may find it helpful to make lists of different multiples.

There are different ways of making four multiples of 4.

12	32	20
4	4	36
8	16	4
36	8	8

It is possible to make six multiples of 3.
Here is one solution, using all ten cards: 3, 9, 12, 45, 60, 78

Some ways of making multiples of other numbers include:

x2	x3	x4	x5	x6	x7	x8	x9	x10
2	3	4	5	96	805	8	9	70
4	9	8	30	54	91	16	18	
6	12	16		18	7	72	27	
8	45	32		30	63	40	36	
10	60			72	42		45	
	78							

QUESTIONS

(?) How many different multiples of 5 can be made? Why?

(?) How many different multiples of 10 can be made? Why?

(?) How can [4] be used for multiples of 3?

(?) Why is it impossible to make more than four multiples of 4?

EXTENSIONS

(→) Try exploring different ways of making four multiples of 4.

(→) Try making other types of numbers, e.g. square numbers, prime numbers, odd and even numbers.

(→) Try making multiples of numbers greater than 10.

Multiples

You will need these cards

0 1 2 3 4 5 6
7 8 9

Choose a set of **multiples** ⟶ **Multiples of 4**

Now make different **multiples of 4**.
Each card may be used only **once**.

1 2
4
8
3 6

four multiples of 4

5 0
7 9

not used

Use the cards to make different **multiples of 3**

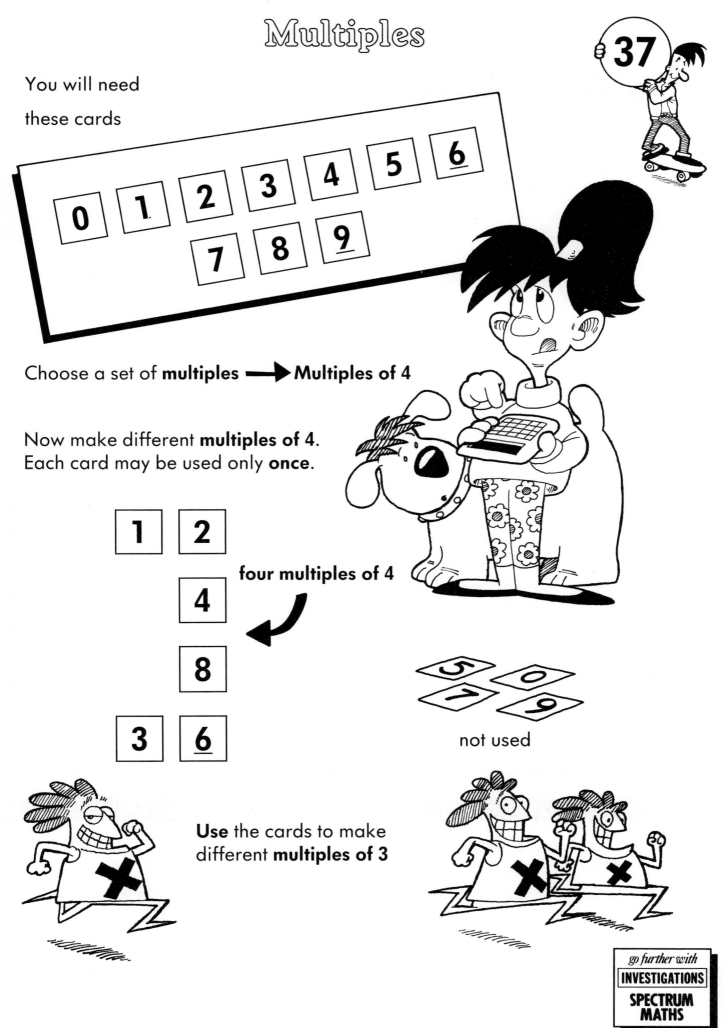

Face to face

NUMBER PATTERNS

Finding different arrangements of the faces of two numbered cubes to make two-digit numbers.

Apparatus

Blank cubes are required so that numbers can be written on the faces.

LEVEL	Profile Component 1				Profile Component 2		
	UA	N	A	M	UA	S	D
1							
2							
3	●		●				
4	●		●		·		
5	●						
6	●						
7							
8							
9							
10							

A3: Number patterns in two-digit numbers.
A4: Generalise patterns in words.

There are 63 different possible two-digit numbers. These can be found by keeping one dice fixed and trying different positions for the other.

Using the 1, 2, 3, 4, 5, 6 cube as the tens digit, these are the different numbers.

14	24	34	44	54	64
15	25	35	45	55	65
16	26	36	46	56	66
17	27	37	47	57	67
18	28	38	48	58	68
19	29	39	49	59	69

Using the 4, 5, 6, 7, 8, 9 cube as the tens digit, these are the different numbers.

41	51	61	71	81	91
42	52	62	72	82	92
43	53	63	73	83	93
44	54	64	74	84	94
45	55	65	75	85	95
46	56	66	76	86	96

These are common to both sets.

QUESTIONS

(?) Which is the smallest/greatest possible number?

(?) Can you make all the numbers between 60 and 70?

(?) Which numbers can be found in two different ways?

EXTENSIONS

(→) Try numbering the cubes differently.

(→) Try with 3 cubes to make three-digit numbers.

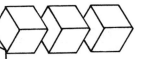

Face to face

You will need

two blank cubes

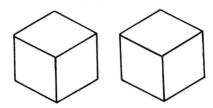

On the faces of one cube write 1 2 3 4 5 6.

On the other cube write 4 5 6 7 8 9.

Put the two cubes together.

These show **17**.

How many different two-digit numbers can you show?

39 Pentagon patterns

SHAPE PATTERNS

Making different patterns based on the regular pentagon.

Apparatus

Use special paper 3 for drawings of regular pentagons.

LEVEL	Profile Component 1				Profile Component 2		
	UA	N	A	M	UA	S	D
1							
2							
3					●		
4					●	●	
5					●		
6					●		
7							
8							
9							
10							

S4: Constructing shapes and patterns.
Rotational symmetry.

Pupils should be encouraged to be accurate in the drawing of the guidelines and also in the colouring of the patterns. Some patterns can be created by using the diagonals.

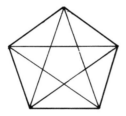  

More intricate patterns can be created by drawing additional guidelines.

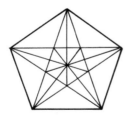  

Pupils could invent names for their designs.
Many designs will have rotational symmetry.

QUESTIONS

(?) Which patterns are symmetrical?

(?) What shapes can you see in each design?

(?) How many different pentagons are there in each design?

EXTENSIONS

(→) Try starting with regular hexagons.

(→) Try cutting out some of the designs.

(→) Try pasting the designs onto the faces of a dodecahedron.

Pentagon patterns

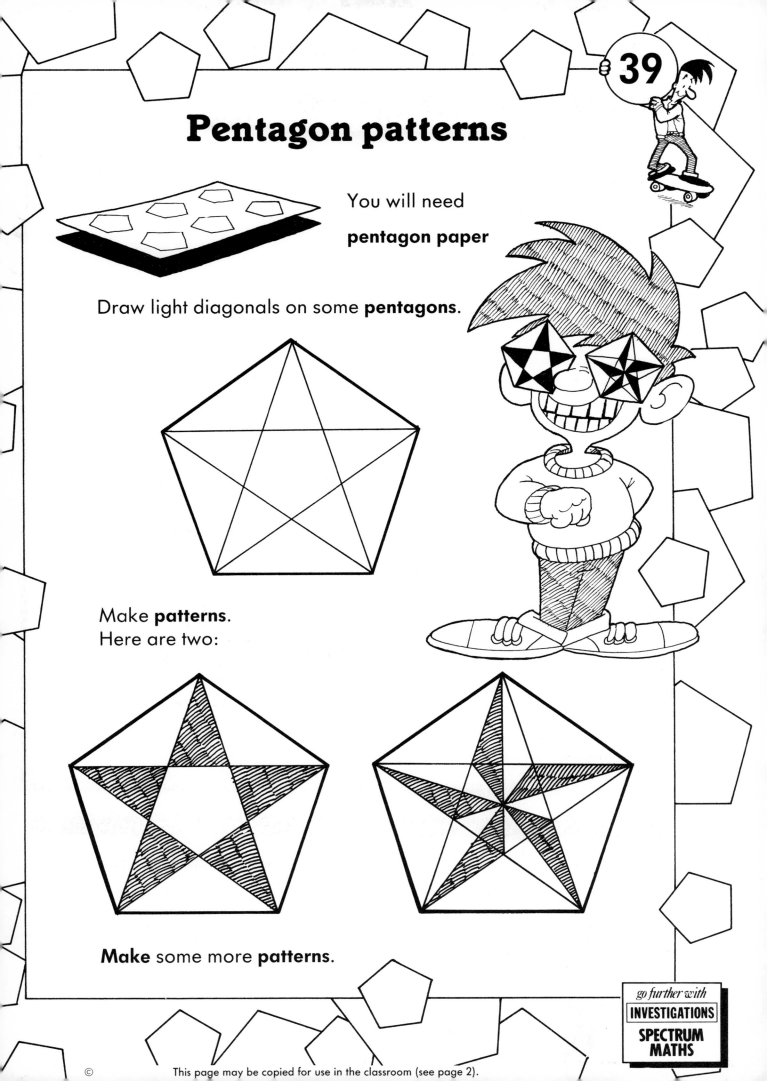

You will need

pentagon paper

Draw light diagonals on some **pentagons**.

Make **patterns**.
Here are two:

Make some more **patterns**.

go further with
INVESTIGATIONS
SPECTRUM MATHS

Remainders

DIVISION

NUMBER PATTERNS

Remainders when dividing by 4. Remainders when dividing by other numbers. Patterns in repeating cycles of digits.

LEVEL	Profile Component 1				Profile Component 2		
	UA	N	A	M	UA	S	D
1							
2							●
3	●	●	●				
4	●	●					
5	●						
6	●						
7							
8							
9							
10							

N3: Remainders.
N4: Division by single-digit numbers.
A3: Number patterns.
D2: Recording outcomes.

Patterns are easier to spot if the numbers are arranged in sequence.
Numbers which give a remainder of 1 are:
     5, 9, 13, 17, 21, 25, 29, 33, . . .
Note the repeating cyclic pattern in the last digits:
     5, 9, 3, 7, 1, 5, 9, 3, . . .
The possible remainders are 0, 1, 2 and 3.

Remainder	Numbers	Repeating pattern in last digits
0	4, 8, 12, 16, 20, 24, 28, 32, . . .	4, 8, 2, 6, 0; . . .
1	5, 9, 13, 17, 21, 25, 29, 33, . . .	5, 9, 3, 7, 1; . . .
2	6, 10, 14, 18, 22, 26, 30, 34, . . .	6, 0, 4, 8, 2; . . .
3	7, 11, 15, 19, 23, 27, 31, 35, . . .	7, 1, 5, 9, 3; . . .

The repeating patterns are identical for numbers with remainders 0 and 2, and also for numbers with remainders 1 and 3.

QUESTIONS

(?) How many different remainders are possible when dividing by 4?

(?) How many different remainders are possible when dividing by 6, 8, 3, . . .?

EXTENSIONS

(→) Try finding remainders when dividing by 6, 7, and so on.

Remainders

Each of these numbers gives a **remainder of 1** when it is **divided by 4**.

5
13
41

FIDO

Find some more numbers that do this.

Investigate numbers that give a **remainder of 2** when they are **divided by 4**.

go further with
INVESTIGATIONS
SPECTRUM MATHS

© This page may be copied for use in the classroom (see page 2).

Special paper 1

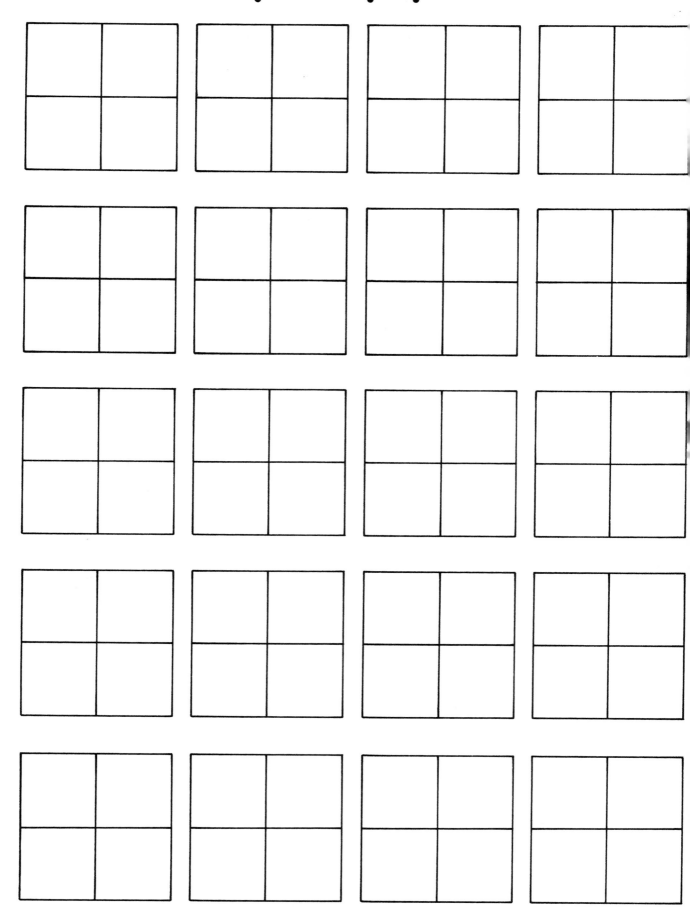

Special paper 2

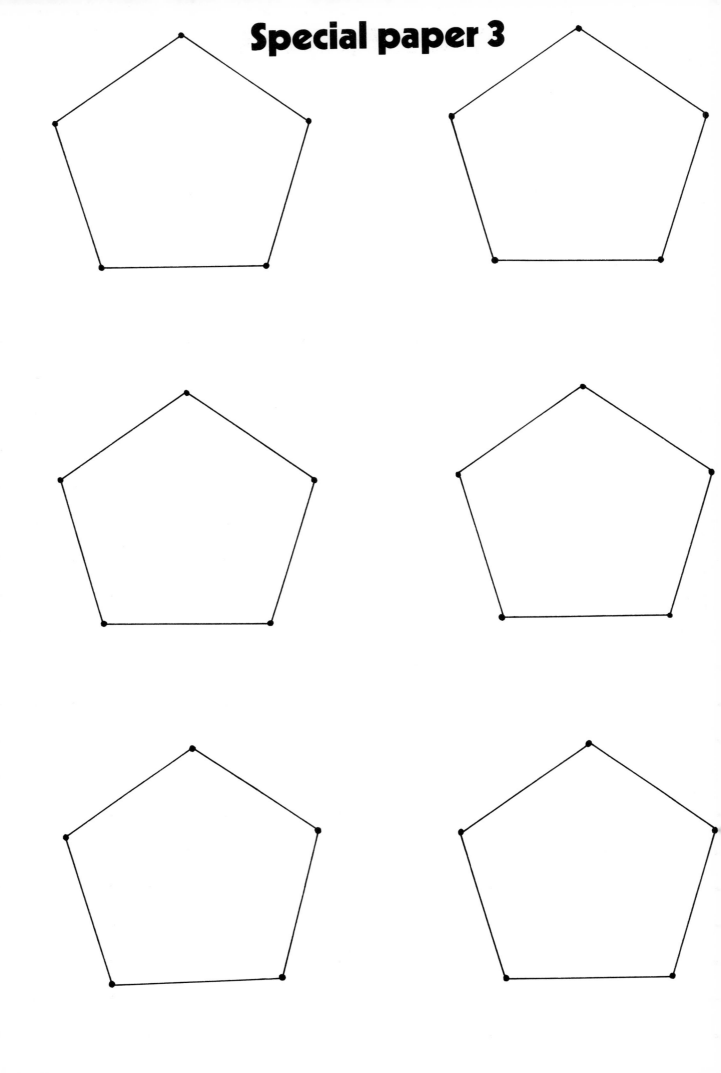

Special paper 4

Special paper 5

Special paper 6